D1128713

THE CHILD IN THE GLASS BALL

THE CHILD
IN THE GLASS BALL

KARIN STENSLAND JUNKER

Translated by Gustaf Lannestock

ABINGDON PRESS   NEW YORK   NASHVILLE

THE CHILD IN THE GLASS BALL

Copyright © 1964 by Abingdon Press
Translated from *De ensamma*, Natur Och Kultur,
Stockholm, 1961

All rights in this book are reserved.
No part of the book may be reproduced in any
manner whatsoever without written permission of
the publishers except brief quotations embodied in
critical articles or reviews. For information address
Abingdon Press, Nashville 2, Tennessee.

Library of Congress Catalog Card Number: 64-10602

SET UP, PRINTED, AND BOUND BY THE
PARTHENON PRESS, AT NASHVILLE,
TENNESSEE, UNITED STATES OF AMERICA

"By this shall all men know that ye are my disciples, if ye have love one to another." JOHN 13:35

I

An unpretentious hotel in Gothenburg would at last offer me the opportunity. When I closed the brown-stained door to room twenty-one I understood at once how it must be. Slowly I walked over to the little desk that was to become my working table; something outside myself guided my steps, it seemed.

Hotel rooms have special qualities of their own; only one door leads in. Except for the maid only one person—the guest himself—has reason to use that door. It is a precious gift this, a door to close.

Outside a persistent west coast fog drove against the window, now in thick wads, now in tattered veils revealing a touch of sky that might eventually turn blue. The curtain fluttered a little at each cutting thrust of wind.

From the hall came sounds of people, people constantly opening doors. I wondered a little at this stubborn desire to open doors when it was such a relief to have them closed.

It was strange; in spite of the many sounds around me they did not take away anything from me. Instead, they gave me a new peace to remember, to look back on. The sounds of a city which is not one's home have a different rhythm; both the town's everyday life and its festivals have another color, the dialect a melody that catches the ear. These differences might not be noticeable to one coming from far away, but to me they were just sufficient to give something I subconsciously had longed for—the interruption of homelife's intimate actuality, a moment of needed reflection, in a city that was not "at home," yet not far enough away to stimulate with exotic strangeness.

It was what might be called undisturbed seclusion. Here I could write down all, exactly as it was—as I now discerned it through the gray west coast haze of February.

And perhaps I might find an answer.

It had been a warm autumn that time—burning late summer sun. The old estate—turned into a pension—was situated on a bay of Lake Mälaren. *Oranier* and *Gyllenkrok* [apples] in heavy ripeness already pushed for space on knotted branches in the dilapidated orchard. The farm and its buildings had been rented out, and from the barns manure fumes permeated the air. The asters bowed their resplendent heads under the rust-yellow umbrage of the tall maples. Each morning the sun rose equally warm and benevolent over the lofty, sturdy oaks. In spite of a fragrance from the approaching decay of withered fields, summer lingered over the vapid, grayish water into which I every day crept from the old, rickety laundry pier, well protected against observation by the tangled reeds along the shore.

All was as it ought to be on a Swedish estate-pension, privately run with dwindling means, during the fall-season's dying days. Mattresses, having lost the springiness of their youth, sagged like pot-bellies; meatballs and stewed carrots served on tables covered with plastic cloth; smell of fried onions in dark hallways; rasping radio news in a gray-brown, sexless sitting room; quiet, complaining conversations about aches and mushrooms. All was as usual.

What, then, had driven me to find this place where everything—from the soiled covers on the dining room chairs to the squeaky beds—bore witness to a speedy economic decline? Was it a subconscious anxiety? I am not unfamiliar with anxiety as such; rather, I am quite intimate with it. And yet, just then there was less reason for apprehension than ever. Why should I not be able to sleep? Why?

At home, therefore, we had agreed upon a change of surroundings for a time. Why not take along some work and go away for a few weeks? Some writing to divert my thoughts, some knitting for the life growing within me. A moderate price—for the sake of the purse.

The woods were that fall rich in mushrooms. I learned to recognize the *riddarmusseronen*, the *ängsvaxskivlingen*, the bishop's mitre, and the creased *tofsskivlingen*, and I proudly displayed my newfound knowledge the Sunday our friends came to visit; they had furnished me the address of the pension, and now we went out together to hunt chanterelles.

But all the time the anxiety was there.

Later I was to recall that even then I was on my guard as it were. Against what? I didn't know. But it was as if in advance I was set on training my memory-functions. I inculcated what seemed to me unusual, without knowing why. Episodes without apparent connection.

My friend's wife, for example.

We were standing in the yard, our mushroom crop displayed on newspapers we had spread over the garden table. Suddenly I happened to meet the look in her eyes; it was burning with a fire I hadn't noticed before. Her voice was vibrating with a fanaticism that was a riddle to me. What was she saying? She was warning me. She was warning me against men, our men, all men.

Many years later, when happenings to come already had

9

taken place, I recalled her metallically fatalistic voice: "Better be careful! You don't know what might happen! No, you don't!" And the fatalism of her voice was not milder that day, much later, when I learned she was ill. I seemed to have found a connection I could not disregard. Yet there was no connection—a wretched paranoiac seeking an escape, peace, an end to persecutions, the morbid triumph of revenge through a cut in the wrist while in the tub, an overdose of sleeping pills—and then the final victory: so deeply have you hurt me that this must happen! No, a logical connection there was not.

Nor was there any connection with the old colonel who sat aged-stiff at the table, his bib around his neck, at the opposite end of the pension dining room.

The colonel also is dead now, like our friend's wife, and he no longer suffers from the shadows he argued with while the soup trickled from the corners of his mouth onto the bib. At that time I had never heard of senile dementia, I knew nothing of all the closed doors society has ready for the colonel and his likes. I thought his conversations were based on reality. And secretly I felt sorry for all his enemies.

Our table conversations were not of the ordinary kind. To call them irrational would be a pale description; they were simply amazing. And I linger over these episodes now because I feel they have their place in my pattern. They belong.

There was still another one who was a part of the pattern, whom I will here call the Inconvenient One—it was above all in that capacity he was to play a small role in my life. A role I later was to remember.

It is not—as I later tried to talk myself into thinking—that all these incidents appear with more clearness because I now know what happened later. No, there was something special with those autumn days, a peculiarly stagnant apprehension. As I walked through the tall, untended grass down to the little laundry pier for my daily swim in the tepid, gray-brown water, I had in my company Fate. I felt it without understanding it. The tall grass brushed against my bare knees in the same way as when I was a child; I recognized the feel. It was as then.

Like most Stockholm families in our circumstances we used to spend our summers in the archipelago. Out there Father owned a so-called paradise for children—a rather good-sized island and a few adjacent islets where our games were played in hectic competition—shivering, blue-frozen swimming events, sailing races, nettle-weeding in the garden beds.

And why do I bring this up now?

The Inconvenient One was indirectly to build a bridge to my childhood land, without my clearly seeing the connection. That is why I must let my thoughts play with him for a moment, and also the personality which so fully dominated my early years—my father. I must linger, partly in the archipelago, partly at Lake Mälaren.

We lived, then, on that island of ours looking out over the Kanholm inlet; here, too, the grass in time grew unattended, as in the pension park—a victim to departing economic affluence, to a change with something vanishing: an old-days' middle-class order.

Everything existed in my childhood archipelago-land; raw, penetrating evening breezes from the inlet; smell of drought; weeds and sun-warm paths; a privy's stacks of weeklies; drooping Yellow Bedstraw; white-nettles; and the Queen's Lace— a more poetic name for Drooping Dog perhaps. The breathlessly hot summer day was filled with lazy salt swims, long mornings of cleaning the nets, waiting hours in the raisin-fragrant store, and the evening's rowing to get the milk at Westerman's across the inlet. The nights were filled with persistent mosquito-buzz above the sheet pulled over the head—nightmarishly sticky while waiting for sleep—or dawn's crimson over the islets toward northeast.

There was even a fear of a more picturesque kind in our summer land; that fear lurked along an old barnhouse wall, inside which a farmhand was said to have hanged himself fifty years earlier.

All this returned to me as I now was tramping through the

11

grass with the new life within me—that grass which ought to have been mowed if anyone had been interested in free hay any longer. Such grass can scratch rather sharply against the legs, and—as in my childhood—perhaps I pulled a blade, put it between my thumbs and blew, creating a muffled, almost hoarse, sound. And perhaps I cautiously looked over my shoulder. Was he after me again?

The Inconvenient One—why was only I his victim? Why must he repeat his misfortune endlessly only at my side, pursuing me after each meal with his splashing coffee cup in obstinate importunity, spluttering his pig-headedness in a shower of saliva over my knitting. Why only I?

So it was to be every day that just I was the recipient of these confidences. After all, I'm not a social worker, am I? But his sort doesn't seem to realize that. It is as if they leeched onto me with their confidences. Anyway, the Inconvenient One took no notice of my reluctance. He never listened when I said I might be in a hurry. He was hard of hearing of course. But still—he might have some consideration. Didn't I have the right to expect that from him?

But no, the Inconvenient One seemed to have no feelings. He only talked and talked. There was no end to what he talked about. He wrote also, he said. Wrote? What did he write?—novels, poems—such trouble. The most difficult of all. Couldn't he have taken up something else?

But he only went right on, he must not have heard my thought. He did hear poorly, wretched soul; I believe I said so . . . moreover, naturally I never spoke my thoughts aloud. Not easy to hear then. Thoughts one can only sense. To sense them one must have feelings.

He was going to write about a deaf person's loneliness, he said. The wall around the deaf. He would write about the laughter one never caught. It might have been he himself that they laughed at—well, how could one know? But one might have one's suspicions.

He would write about how it was at school. The first story he had been asked to read when starting the third grade. It was called "Good Morning, Block-head!" Just he had been

12

asked to read it before the whole class. And, oh, how they had laughed that time, those little fellows. Did I think this was right? Society really ought to have some obligations . . . .

But it wasn't like that in school any longer, I suggested. Modern educational methods were quite different, I thought.

But that story was still in many readers for children. And it was awfully funny, didn't I think? He leaned toward me until I could feel his breath. Also a touch of perspiration.

I apologized. I regretted I didn't have any more time. I had some work to do. Time was fleeing and nothing accomplished.

Well, he could understand that. He, too, knew how it was when one was writing. He was a writer himself—didn't I remember he had told me?

A writer also? But I wasn't writing. It must have been in his imagination.

Of course, I did! Even with his bad hearing he was aware of the rattle of my typewriter.

Oh, that. Well, it wasn't writing exactly. I was only working on some translations, something of no consequence. And I was editing a report on building research. It wasn't really creative writing. Only a kind of proofreading. But it had to be finished, like everything else. So naturally I couldn't sit and talk the time away.

But I was writing something else, he insisted. He could see it. He was aware of it in people, he emphasized. They had another understanding. About things that were different.

Well, many years ago I did write, I finally admitted reluctantly. A couple of bad books I wouldn't wish to talk about. Could one really stop writing once one had started? Was that possible? Well, if one doesn't have anything to write about. But those books—weren't they published? Well, yes. But that didn't mean anything.—But the reviews?—Well, so and so.—You do write, then?—No, I don't.—Who published your books?—Good Lord! I believe the publisher went bankrupt—anyway, there are no possibilities . . . no possibilities. . . . But society ought to have responsibility.

Well, perhaps. How could I know? I pushed the Incon-

venient One away. Next meal he would come with his manu-
scripts, I knew he would. He would force me to read, take a
position. He would force me to promise to say a good word
for him to my publisher.

I really didn't have the time.

It wasn't my fault that his hearing was bad. It wasn't I
who had asked him to read "Good Morning, Block-head!"
I had been as little as he when that had happened.

I wanted definitely to be left alone. I knew only too well
the trend these conversations would take, because they were
too closely related to my childhood. I couldn't take any more.
I hadn't asked to share confidences. On the contrary—I was
paying my room and board for one reason—to be left alone.
To be left outside what didn't concern me.

Society ought to have an obligation, he was saying again.
He was talking about discrimination; he was lifting his fist
and dropping it against the table top. The coffee cup jumped,
and the saucer was smeared as usual. Society ought to get
him a worthy position. Didn't he have the same right to work
as other people even though he couldn't hear as well? After
all, he wasn't an invalid.

Invalid. I had had that word around me my whole life.
Couldn't I be spared it now? And again my childhood-land
came to the fore. . . .

❧

My father had suffered from rheumatoid arthritis since he
was seventeen. It had come on unexpectedly. One day when
out hunting on the estate where he had dreamed away his
childhood summers—sometimes sailing peacefully across the
Björkfjärden, sometimes stalking Redskins among Korp-
berget's wild cliffs, sometimes on horseback—then the inexplicable had happened, suddenly. He felt as if a sharp ax
had hit him in the hollows behind his knees. He sank to the
ground. He used to relate how his hunting dog stayed at his
side, howling persistently, until aid finally came.

Father became a lifetime-invalid, more helpless than most.
His early years were those of a well-to-do rheumatic. The

14

spas of the Continent superseded one another, as did the doctors. One gymnastic method after another was tried, electric currents through the legs, stretching paraphernalia, diets of nuts and other vegetables, mud baths, dry desert air during Egyptian winters, warm springs of Ischia, clay-packs, radiation, sun baths, and taking the waters at different places. Constantly on journeys he was hunting for a remedy that no one could find for him. Aswan and Cairo, Naples and Florence, Aix-les-Bains, Skodsborg, Mösseberg and Loka, Carlsbad and Bordeaux—nowhere could they arrest the disease spreading through his joints.

The naked fact was that the sickness stubbornly endured all the modern applications of that age and survived in magnificent imperturbability. And when a new age dawned, with new methods that might have given relief—well, then Father no longer was the well-to-do invalid; by then he was the bankrupt invalid, and both golden salt and cortisone were as much out of his reach as the mud baths and the warm springs had been ineffective.

But Father's intellect blossomed in his infirm, crippled body. He had an intellectual sense of responsibility which, I regretfully must admit, I did not inherit. Ambition? Well, perhaps one might call it that. I would rather say he suffered from a sort of intellectual kleptomania. He must pick up, get hold of, possess all the knowledge that touched his path. Even during his final days he was studying a radio course in Spanish, because he felt ashamed of the lack in his education that had prevented him from reading Cervantes in the original.

Invalid.

Doesn't it come from the Latin *invalidus*—worthless, valueless? Was my father really worthless? Valueless, perhaps, not usable coinage. What is alien is perhaps not usable coinage. One cannot pay with an Indian rupee at a milk bar in Sweden. This is too obvious to be mentioned; who would dream of it?

But worthless? That is something other than valueless. The Indian rupee has a considerable value in another place. Much greater than a Swedish crown. The rupee might mean

15

the difference between life and death. It is far from worthless in another country.

On another level.

Only, one must save the rupee until one gets to that other place, the other level. After all, four hundred million people live in that place where the valueless coin has value. Not so small a part of the earth's population either.

So it is, then, with the word *invalidus*, invalid. An invalid just happens to be valueless in the place where I am. Could this perhaps be because of the limitations of the place? And would perhaps a time come when the limitations are obliterated? When all coin is valuable everywhere?

Invalid, then, is a word to evoke many thoughts in someone willing to attempt an interpretation. Mightn't one suspect that my father would be familiar with that word, intimate with the meaning of *invalidus*?

No, my father burned with too singeing, too consuming a fire. And his flame singed also us, our childhood, our family life. Could anything else have been possible?

That is why I recall my childhood as a series of impotent outbursts—against something that I never was in a position to view through the tempered, polished glass of sober objectivity. Especially the difficult years—they stand out—those years when he fluttered about helplessly in a no-man's-land, economically wing-clipped, outside the accepted order of a paycheck the last of the month, telephone and electricity the tenth, the grocer the fifteenth, time payments and interest the twentieth, the maid on the last—and so the circle closed. To find oneself outside all these dates is difficult enough for a bankrupt person who has his health. In this case a poor one has a definite advantage; the poor one is accustomed to it.

Father was not accustomed to poverty. He never learned. And as he never could gain the health that would have entitled him to a place in line for jobs available in those days, neither was he placed in the right reference category. He had only his own category. His frustration became an outburst of protest and anguish. And the outburst kept burning closer and closer to the explosion point.

Yet, I loved Father. I loved my mother with passion. I recall my pride when Father let the chauffeur drive me to the fine, noble-girls' school which it was thought I should attend, in spite of all. He kept the car robe pulled high over his shoulders. I was grateful. No one could see the crooked arms, the stiff, spread fingers. The girls could see only his fine features, his grand profile, the clear-blue, alive eyes. They could see the big, red-brown Buick town car and the chauffeur in his blue-gray livery. How close to, or how far from, this highly polished radiator lay the ruin caused by overdue loans was in those days entirely outside my comprehension. Nor could one read on our equipage how long the chauffeur had been waiting for his pay. I felt only the intoxication of luxury when the other girls looked and asked.

It could not be expected that I would understand the roots of his outbursts. This person—part and parcel of my earliest, most elementary impressions—how could I comprehend that he in some way might differ from other fathers? During one's first years of consciousness most people see their own home only from the inside. It would have been totally alien to me to see Father as "a poor invalid" who—through humiliating considerations by outsiders—belonged in a department marked "Fragile! Handle with care!"

When, as quite little, I learned a few things that hardly were included in the curriculum of a well-behaved girl—how to tie a man's tie neatly, how to pull up the overcoat at the neck, like a real valet, how to part a man's stiff neck-hair, or tie the laces on a man's shoe—it never occurred to me that this was anything outside the ordinary. Something other girls weren't familiar with. I had nothing to compare with—little girls didn't talk of such matters.

I had no perspectives. It lay outside my understanding that Father's anger might have to do with something other than Mother, us children, or our needs. Moreover, how could a little child differentiate between the anger over an insolvable situation, a not-self-inflicted condition, and the anger against a person? This could not be expected of a child.

Therefore Father by and by was to experience consequences

17

from his helpless outbursts that he never could have suspected. More and more often, I—his only daughter and the apple of his eye—was to take a position against him, against the strange, apparently irresistible forces he had let loose, and which constantly threatened the security of my childhood. Because it was so irrational that the very thing Father was most incensed against—life's denial of the ability to face problems under the same conditions as other individuals—just this very equality I, in my narrow corner, took for granted that he possessed. And, therefore, I saw him, plain and simple, as any other person, with tremendous and inexplicable demands on his near and dear, a person who had been careless enough to squander too much money; a person devoid of any consideration, lacking self-control, allowing his family to suffer from his shortcomings.

During my grown years, away from my childhood home, my perspective changed and my range of vision widened, I would learn the difference. Only then would I realize our dilemma, recognize how Father kept fighting his hopeless battle to gain from others what I so long had given him automatically—equality without compassion.

I have not related this about my father in order to find an excuse for what later happened in my relationship with the Inconvenient One. I have related it only as a kind of explanatory background. And before I leave Father I must therefore relate a little episode, the meaning of which I did not understand until many years after its happening.

It was long after our livery-clad chauffeur had vanished from the scene. Nearly always Father would take a taxi, but there were times when he used the streetcar. The streetcar was all right, he insisted, good enough for anyone willing to use this means of transportation. None of us children thought of, or could have realized, how much effort a ride on the streetcar cost him. It only dawned on us one day, after which his streetcar rides came to an end. That day he had returned terribly depressed. He wouldn't tell us why. He had never shown annoyance when people stared at him, although he must have felt it. But this was something else. Something serious must have happened on the streetcar.

At last it came out. He related, sadly, that something terrible had taken place. He would never again be able to ride the streetcar, because the worst possible had happened—a young lady had offered him her seat in the car.

The very thought of it.

※

It was the noon hour, and I was walking according to my habit through the grass down toward the lake. The heat shimmered over the railroad tracks which I must cross to reach the laundry pier. It was like a July heat; September was making a last desperate effort to retain the summer that had fled, never to return. Suddenly I felt that tightening anxiety within me. Yes, I was thinking mechanically, it isn't spring, it isn't summer any longer. I'm already over thirty and carry my third child. No longer a youth.

I threw the bathrobe over my shoulder, looked down the railway. No, at this time of day no train would disturb the pastoral idyll. The old barn next to the tracks hid in its decayed loneliness the blackened hay of many summers ago. Suddenly I shuddered. Had something moved back there?

The road sloped down to the pier, the reeds hid me. I peered again. Was there someone behind me?

Nonsense. Of course no one was there.

How strange that I almost shivered, although my dress stuck to my back from the heat. I must be careful and take only a short dip today. I mustn't catch a cold so late in my time. A cold? There was no reason for it in this summer heat.

I struggled out of my sticky dress, looked again toward the swaying reeds. How one's imagination could run wild at times.

I pulled off the last garments. How could it be so balmy in September?

When I descended the rickety little ladder made of decaying boards which the pension-owner had provided as a sacrifice for his guests, I noticed the reeds definitely move. Someone was there then.

Heavens! Someone must have followed me after all.

At once I felt unable to take a single stroke. I caught hold of the edge of the pier, pushed myself up by my arms, stretched for my robe and grabbed it. What if it did get wet? I didn't care. I fumbled as I climbed the ladder, clumsy as I was from my expectancy. In one way or another I had managed to put on my robe.

Suddenly he stood in front of me, the Inconvenient One. His laughter was a little unsteady, searching for community. I only stared. Fear had taken hold of me. I held onto the robe with clenched fists. I must have looked ridiculous in my fright and the wet robe straining. I wanted to yell, do something, run away, hit him, or anything. But I only stood still and stared.

He had come quite close by now.

"Shame . . . have you no decency!" Somewhere from inside me a sort of voice escaped at last.

"Sshhame?" he said. "Why?"

Suddenly I had a strong urge to laugh; his s's had such a ridiculous slur.

"Sshhould I feel asshhamed becausshh I love you? I can't help it. That'sshh the way it issh."

I noticed the irresolution of his dangling hands; I noticed a narrow band of perspiration drops across his nose; I noticed how wrinkled his pants were hanging around his legs. My heart no longer beat so wildly.

"Nonsense!" I said, in sober emphasis. "This is ridiculous! You must know I'm married and soon in my eighth month!"

He took a step toward me, and now my fear overwhelmed me anew. I bent down quickly and picked up my clothes with one hand. Then I pushed him aside roughly and started running.

I ran up the slope, the grass rasping my legs as always. But this time I was not aware of any forgotten fragrance of memories of childhood-summers. I only ran, the skirts of my straining robe fluttering around my legs, a frightened hen, perhaps, or a waddling duck.

There was a throbbing within me—or was it his steps I

heard behind me? Oh, Lord! What if it would be a miscarriage! I stumbled across the tracks; at last I reached the gate opening. Well! Up there sat the white mansion, with its scaling plaster.

A few steps more. Would I dare look? I stopped on the gravel. Now I could hear. Thump, thump, thump. It was my own heart. I turned stiffly, as if I had lumbago, or a stiff neck. Through the dark foliage of the tall linden trees, white-warm sunrays strained through, forming a glittering silk border in a crisscross pattern in the green dimness of the estate driveway.

No one.

The entrance road was empty. No one was after me. I remained standing a moment. Had the whole thing been my imagination?

Slowly I walked across the yard, through the veranda, up to my room, locked the door.

Perhaps it had only been a dream, a hallucination.

I sat down on the edge of the bed, dried my forehead, looked about, probing as it were. Had this happened? Of course not. It was only imagined. Pregnant women are inclined to imagine a lot.

At last the dinner bell sounded. I went down, hesitantly.

The Inconvenient One sat at his table as usual. He refused neither the stew nor the apple tart with milk. Nothing wrong with his appetite, apparently.

But he never lifted his eyes from the plate. He sat so quietly I was beginning to wonder if he actually was there. And after the meal he did not come with his coffee cup as usual. He just vanished, no one asked where.

During the following nights I locked the door to my room and took sleeping tablets. But a night came when the tablets had no effect. I lay there turning on the bumpy mattress, tried placing the pillows in strategic positions, rose and drank a mouthful of water, lit the bed lamp, blew it out, and lit it again.

Then, suddenly, I heard it.

From somewhere came muffled sobs. Hollow, hoarse sobs. A man's sobs.

Such sobs I had not heard for a very long time. To be exact, not since exchanging my parental home for the nest of the newly-married. I remembered my father's nocturnal, remorseful crying after one or another of his outbursts.

The sobs now, like then, were a maimed man's protests. I took an extra strong dose and went to sleep finally.

❧

A few days later our friend and his family came to visit and to enjoy a last chanterelle hunt.

No, I had stopped taking my swims, I said, when they asked if I still "sported down to the lake every day." It was just as well, they agreed. I ought to be careful. Well, I did think it had grown a little cooler now. Summer must at last be ended. It was to be expected. It couldn't last forever. Not even this unusual Indian Summer could last forever.

After dinner—I believe around five o'clock, but I'm not quite sure—my friends and I were listening to the radio. We heard in consternation the newscaster break in to say that Folke Bernadotte had been murdered in Israel. Folke Bernadotte was our Chief Scout, respected, beloved, and a symbol of goodwill and obvious help. What would now happen to the Scout Movement?

What indeed?

Little did I suspect at that time that even the name of Folke Bernadotte would help form a part of the pattern now weaving during these late-summer days.

Part of the pattern that was to be mine.

❧

My departure was imminent, my translation had been completed. One of my last few days in the pension had brought a young girl with pale features, lusterless hair, and eyes without color. She had unobtrusively joined the guests; perhaps she suffered from some anemic malady. The hostess had placed her at the Inconvenient One's table.

When I was taking my farewell walk under the linden trees I suddenly espied the anemic one, strolling along. The next moment the Inconvenient One emerged from a side door of the old manor. They started on their walk side by side; there was an air of engagement, of home-custom, in their way of meeting up. Was I wrong, or had he taken her arm?

On the train home to Stockholm my companion again was Anxiety. It was now at home in me, and it resembled greatly a premonition.

II

The labor pains were now so frequent that they began being hard to master. What time was it? The hours dragged that Saturday night, slowly, slowly, and each hour an infinite number of long, long minutes. Would midnight never come?

A delivery room—is there anything more bare, more desolate? Is one ever more exposed? The blank walls, in all their sterility, keep a cold watch around the hard slaughterbench where hour after hour must be endured with ever increasing pains. No one is there, only the pain; no hand to hold.

Now and then someone peeked in through the door—an eternity between each time, it seemed. The clock ticked on and on, the hands moved over an artless, functional face; not a single little decorative line around the numerals, not a single little flower; only straight, black figures on the shiny, professional disk.

Again a nurse looked in through the door.

Such a nurse seemed hardly real; in gauze mask, packed in

24

all-white anonymity, fluttering back there at the door, one might wonder if she really existed. One could never be sure. A hurried mumble was the only thing one caught from the door ajar. I couldn't see from her eyes whether she smiled or was annoyed over the time I took for a procedure like this.

"Is it quite difficult? Shouldn't we try some twilight sleep, Mrs. Junker?" It was her voice, it was real. She existed then. "Why not try it?"

"No, thank you. Not for me. I'll wait a little longer. Kind of you, Nurse."

I had made my decision; perhaps it was a ridiculous one, but it was what I wanted.

Tomorrow would be the First Sunday in Advent.

This baby must be born on the First Sunday in Advent, such was my decision. My child, our child, must be a little Sunday-child. And not only that—our child would be a First Sunday in Advent-child. No one could any longer prevent me from having it so. The twilight sleep apparatus stood close by me; with each new pain the temptation increased. Yes, I remembered its relief in the previous times. I remembered the wonderful indifference. It didn't kill the pains, not entirely. But one felt them as something irrelevant, something outside oneself. Something was happening, but one didn't bother.

But no, I wasn't going to succumb. I would bear a Sunday-child for the family. I would wait till twelve o'clock before using that apparatus. I knew that twilight sleep might hasten the labor. But this time I would decide for myself, take fate in my own hands.

What were they doing at home now? It was eleven, they must have gone to bed by now. Perhaps they had been sitting listening to the radio for a while, playing cards maybe, or enjoying the first Christmas oranges.

Oh! Now came a pain again. It was more intense this time, but I mustn't give in. Since I had managed this long I ought to hang on this last hour.

"The time drags, Nurse . . ."

Her eyes smiled above the white gauze mask, I believe.

She was not so unreal any more—she was there beside me—her cool hand felt my pulse. Her voice was friendly, calm. No anxiety with such a nurse at one's side.

"Wouldn't it be nice with a little gas, after all?"

"Thank you, Dear, I'll wait. You see, Nurse. . . ." Should I tell her? Well, why not? A nurse must often get confidences about one thing or another. "You see, Nurse, . . . it would be so nice to have a . . . a little Advent-child. Could you understand? After twelve o'clock it will be the First Sunday in Advent. I thought I would try."

"Well, well—take it easy then."

"I thought I would wait with the gas until after twelve. I've a feeling it goes much faster if one takes it, doesn't it?"

She stood quite still now, and I could see that her eyes were kind. Suddenly she stroked me gently across the forehead, nodded, and pushed the apparatus out of the room.

"Ring for me at twelve," she said, and nodded again. Now I was sure that she smiled under her mask.

❧

The minute hand crept toward twelve at last. It was getting more and more difficult. Good to be alone; no one need hear. Hear how difficult it could be.

What a silly idea to place a big clock on the wall facing a woman in labor. What was the object? A clock with a minute hand now racing across the numerals, now again creeping at a snail's pace. Ridiculous.

Well, of course, they must know the exact time—the hour, the minute, the second, when the miracle of birth occurs. For everything must be recorded. In a hospital one must keep account of those things. One must know exactly the moment —the day, the hour, the minute—of birth or death.

And now it was twelve o'clock. A child would soon be born, a Sunday-child born on the First Sunday of Advent this year.

I reached for the bell.

"It's a girl! Congratulations, Mrs. Junker! A fine girl!"

"A girl?"

26

"Weren't you hoping it would be a girl, Mrs. Junker?"

"Yes, of course," I said, still only half-conscious. "Nothing wrong with girls, is there?"

Was I disappointed? Had I been hoping for a boy as an Advent-gift? I don't know. I never thought of such things. As if a boy would be more welcome than a girl. It has always seemed a little silly to me, that male self-assurance, apparent in birth announcements reading: "And it is a boy!"

I often wonder about such announcements. A human life has entered our world, and I feel that something indeed much more important has taken place than just this: "And it is a boy!"

"What was that noise out there, Nurse? It sounded as if someone had dropped a child. What could it be?"

I thought I had heard running steps. And now a baby was yelling loudly somewhere. It sounded like a sea gull.

"It's nothing, only your little girl announcing her arrival, Mrs. Junker."

"Why does she yell like that, Nurse?"

"It's good for her to cry."

"But don't you hear—it sounds like a gull, a sea gull?"

"I guess most babies sound that way."

"Like a gull?"

The nurse laughed. "Maybe they do."

"Have you read *The Seagull?*"

"What's that? Hand me those scissors. Thank you! *The Seagull?* What is it?"

"It's a play by Chekhov. Are you familiar with it?"

"No, I don't think so. Now pull on this string a little, like that, thank you."

"It's really a very sad play—it's about a gull, a sea gull that died. And a young girl."

"Now you're talking nonsense, Mrs. Junker. The gas must have gone to your head!" The nurse laughed heartily. "Well, you got your Advent-child anyway. Just as you wanted it, Mrs. Junker."

"But why does she cry so, my little sea gull? What are they doing to her?"

"They're bathing her. Getting her in order to come and see her mamma."

"I'm surprised you haven't heard about *The Seagull*. The young girl, well, really about the girl and a gull . . . something symbolic . . . anyway, things don't go very well for the girl. In fact, everything goes wrong. And the sea gull dies."

"Now, you mustn't talk so much, Mrs. Junker. What you need is a real good rest. Ah, here is the little life! Isn't she cute?"

The nurse showed me the white bundle.

"Can I keep her here with me for a while?"

The nurse placed the bundle beside me in the bed. She didn't cry any more like a gull; she was quiet and contented. The little face was reddish, with white down on cheeks and head. The spindly, delicately pink fingers opened and closed. I recognized those funny little wavy motions of the fingers; I had felt them within me these last months, felt them grow in intensity each day.

"Oh, Nurse—have you called my husband?"

"Yes, Mrs. Junker."

"What did he say?"

"He said he was pleased that all went so well. He asked how you were and said he would be in soon."

"Nurse!"

"Yes, Mrs. Junker?"

"She is sweet, though, isn't she?"

"Yes, a darling."

"But I think she's especially sweet—look, Nurse! Isn't she an unusually beautiful child, my little, little gull! My little Advent-girl!"

The nurse looked dutifully, then she bent closer to the tiny bundle, lifted the light blanket a little. Thoughtfully she stood so for a few moments.

"Yes, Mrs. Junker, now that I look at her closely she is really terribly sweet."

"May I come in and talk for a few moments with a real mother?" It was Elizabeth, the chief nurse of the ward who

28

had come into my room and was leaning against the edge of the bed.

"Aren't your other patients real mothers?" I asked in surprise.

"Some, yes. But so many are dissatisfied. You see, in my ward we have so many 'switch-offs,' and so many who hadn't wanted a child—some already have too many, or perhaps didn't want a child but couldn't get rid of it. Yes, Mrs. Junker, I sometimes wonder what life is all about. Especially when I think of the 'switch-offs,' the abortions. So many lately."

"How strange. I couldn't imagine what it would be like to have a child I hadn't wanted. Or destroy one that is on the way. I don't believe I could survive anything like that. I have longed intensely for all my children. I always blossom when expecting."

The nurse laughed. We both laughed.

"I'm immensely proud of my children," I said. "And each one has been equally longed for. And this little gull—to be really honest, we've waited for her the longest, and perhaps, therefore, we're more happy over her than any of the others. We would have liked to have had her long ago. Well, you can't always control such matters. In confidence, Nurse, the gull is actually a little love-child."

The nurse made ready to leave. "I'm glad to hear things like that. I'm sure she'll bring you much joy—just because she was so longed for. I predict extra great joy from her, Mrs. Junker!"

"But all children bring joy, Nurse!"

"This little girl more than any of them; I just feel it in my blood."

The nurse left, and I watched the door as it slowly closed behind her. It sounded like a sigh.

Much, much later I was to notice that there were episodes from those early days of this baby which emerged from the forgotten past, more vividly than is usual with memories of our children's babyhood. Episodes not in themselves particularly remarkable except for the fact that I had not forgotten them.

I remember the days between Christmas and New Year; she was only a few weeks old, four to be exact. Her older sister, Lena, was four years, tender in her dignified solicitations for the baby's welfare, with not a trace of jealousy and quite worthy of confidence. Then Lena came down with the measles, suddenly and violently; her fever rose alarmingly, and I called our doctor.

"Nothing to worry about; the crisis is passed; she'll pull through without trouble; keep her quiet as long as possible. But what about the baby?"

"The baby? She isn't sick. She has her own room in the other end of the house. She's as well as can be, nothing to worry about her."

"How old is she now? Measles can be dangerous for a baby."

"She's four weeks, but I give her the breast, and I think that's the best protection there is against the measles. I'll be careful when I tend to her, and then, she's in the other end of the house—there should be no worry about contagion."

"But measles are the most contagious of all children's diseases, and could be one of the most dangerous. It penetrates through walls, through the whole house. We had better inoculate her. To be on the safe side."

"But do you think it's necessary to inoculate such a little mite? When I give her the breast, Doctor?"

The doctor shrugged his shoulders: "Well, well. It's not for me to decide. It's your baby. All I can say is that measles can be fatal to a four weeks old baby."

As I followed him to her room, I felt a little ashamed of myself; it was most considerate of the doctor to think of our baby. Yet, as we stood beside the crib, it escaped me again: "Is it really important, Doctor? What a shame to disturb her, she's sleeping so soundly."

The way he looked at me told all: he just couldn't understand me; a sensible person worried about a prick in the skin.

"It only takes a second."

I don't know myself what had gotten into me: I trembled all over as I exposed her little arm. It was as if someone was trying to prevent me from doing this. Ridiculous, of course. But I controlled myself and watched silently as the needle penetrated the thin little arm, the baby skin quite tough and resistant.

I forgot the incident immediately. The measles left our house, Lena was soon up again, the baby didn't get them, nor Sten, the boy.

But long afterward I would recall episodes like this one in the futile search for causes.

⚜

I remember another incident, entirely different. I was busy with the baby in my room when someone appeared outside and knocked on the window. I looked up—there stood Sten, our seven-year-old boy, red-nosed, covered with snow, pointing eagerly through the window to show his pal—the pale, dark-eyed, handsomely tall boy from across the street—that he had a baby sister.

I picked up the child and walked over to the window.

Sten looked at his pal—see now, it is true, we have a real little baby, see for yourself!

I swung the baby up and down before the window, pretended to wave with her little hand, when suddenly something choked in my throat: my son, our big boy, he was so proud of his little sister. I swallowed a few times.

Later I was to remember this too, how I was forced to fail him in his pride. I don't believe he himself has ever thought about it. But I have never been able to forget the eager eyes of the seven-year-old, the proud gestures outside my window that snowy afternoon.

⚜

"Listen to me, Bengt. I can't help it—I'm afraid."

"What are you afraid of?"

"I've got something on my mind."

"Don't get ideas in your head. What is it now?"

"I, I . . . it's come over me that we're going to lose our little girl."

31

"What's that you say? Why should we lose her? She's as healthy as a hazelnut!"

"I don't know what it is. I just feel it in my bones. I know it's stupid—but I'm afraid."

⚜

"What name do you think we should give her?"

We had just taken down the Family Record from its shelf, a tall, narrow book with white leather binding, and we had looked up the various branches of the family tree, beginning with old Skipper Junker of Torekov. There were so many interesting, sonorous, old-fashioned names: Gunnela, Karna, Botilda.

Before Lena was born Bengt mentioned a name he had found in the Record: if it were a girl—how would I like it?

I don't remember why I that time raised an objection to the name he mentioned; it hit me like a cold wind, a strange feeling that I had seen the name in the Record, used only once, with a small cross before it, framed by two dates not far apart. Yes, the name was beautiful, but in some way I was afraid of it. And I had told Bengt so without further explanation; only that I thought it had been the name of someone who had died while little.

We didn't discuss the name any further at that time; Bengt liked it, and I too thought it was nice. But when I raised my peculiar objection he immediately gave in.

This time it was different. We again picked that name in the Record; and this time I had a definite feeling that it was the only suitable name. Of course, so we must name her, this little lass of ours. A beautiful name, rather unusual, one that would go well with our last name. Strangely enough, now I was unable to locate the page in the Record where I thought I had seen a cross before the name of someone who had lived only a short time.

I didn't understand why I had hesitated the first time; now there was no doubt in my mind.

We would call her Boel. Of course, she must also have a

32

few extra names—Maria, after her father's mother, Elisabet, after her mother's mother.

Boel Maria Elisabet Junker.

✣

It was only after Whitsun, when Boel was more than six months old, that I first had a warning. Possibly it was my imagination, but I don't think so. The change took place during Whitsuntide. I remember the holidays so well—Boel had her first illness, which caused me a new worry, and this time with real reason. She had always been a good baby; we had hardly heard her cry except when she was hungry.

Now she was lying in her bed and threw her head back and forth with a plaintive, doleful whine. I took her temperature, but it wasn't abnormally high. It was high, as it is with children of that age. But it wasn't the fever that worried me; it was her behavior. She bent her head backwards and raised her body in an arch. Could it be appendicitis? Was she suffering from pain somewhere else? She cried as if in utter despair, and as if all the pain in the world had come upon her.

I called the doctor. Our regular doctor was away, but I got the "doctor on duty." I remember how glad I was when he said he would be right over. I knew it might be my imagination, but he thought it might be serious. It was Whitsunday, our joyous spring holiday, yet when he arrived he was dressed in deep mourning. This gave me a shock. Later I learned that he had just lost his mother, and I felt I should not have troubled him.

"No, this is not a common cold; her throat isn't red, not in the least. I don't know what it could be. No, it can't be her bowels, no tension. Strange. She seems to have pains somewhere. Does she always cry like this?"

"She never cries, Doctor. She is an unusually quiet child. I don't understand why she tosses her head that way and arches her body."

"Well, it's not a spasm—it wouldn't make her act like that. This is something else. She seems to have a pain in her head."

The doctor wrote out a prescription for some sulfa preparation, and we exchanged a few words about her care for the next few days. I apologized for having disturbed him under the circumstances, but he insisted I call him if I felt in the least concerned.

The doctor left.

The fever went down rather quickly. But she still cried in her plaintive way for a few days and tossed her head back and forth. Then she grew quiet again; her head lay as it should on the little pillow.

❧

"Boel! Hello Boel! Look! Look what I have here!"

I was shaking a silver rattle in front of her, up and down, back and forth. Slowly Boel's eyes followed the motion. When she hit the rattle I wasn't sure if it was by accident. A doubtful smile played over her face.

"Darling Boel, smile for Mamma! Let me see your smile! Boel, sweet, where are your eyes! Here, look at Mamma! Don't look back there in the corner! Smile ever so little, my sweet!"

I lifted Boel high in the air, swung her as one does with babies to make them smile. But. . . .

It was something—something had happened. Now I noticed it. It had come after her illness at Whitsun. Before, Boel had prattled as others, babbled, gurgled. Hadn't she smiled . . . smiled exactly like the other children used to do at that age when I picked them up? Perhaps she hadn't quite as happy a temperament as they, but there had been no perceptible difference as far as I could tell.

This was something new, and with it had come a new fear, without name, without form, without degree: I noticed that she did not smile very often.

"What a wonderful baby! She never cries. And so sweet! What a splendid child!"

How often I heard those words.

Of course, our Boel was a fine girl. They were right. I persuaded myself they were right. But, inside, my fear grew ever stronger. I remembered my premonitions. Purely superstition?

34

"Smile, sweety, smile! Why do you turn your head when Mamma comes? Don't you like Mamma?"

Something had come between the two of us, something intangible. Was it a wall, a barrier? Or was it a chasm, dark and mysterious, deepening ever more?

I couldn't get at it. There was nothing definite. Her development followed the chart I had been presented in the hospital for a mother to watch: weight, height, the appearance of the first tooth, ability to sit, and all the rest. Nothing reasonable existed for my fear. Why did it persist?

She was sweeter than ever, her lashes were longer than other babies', the eyes had a touch of green, curls were beginning to form on her head.

What was it then that was taking place?

Our older children and we parents had been very close to each other, and our closeness had increased at that very age. But how was it with Boel?

Between Boel and us the contact seemed to diminish, fade. We could not catch her eyes. Her look was somewhere else. When she smiled it was as though she was smiling at some secret hidden from us.

Was it perhaps a question of temperament, disposition? Indeed, among our relatives some were more reserved than others. Perhaps Boel had such a reserve, plain and simple. *Noli me tangere*, don't come too close. What was wrong about that? It could hardly be considered a great shortcoming; a kind of shyness one might call it. Nothing wrong with that.

"Boel, my sweety, my darling little girl—smile just a little for Mamma, just a little!"

❧

One evening our singing group was at our house—we had a small glee club in those days, and we used to practice Madrigals at our house on Monday evenings. The singing was over, tea was being served, but first I had to go upstairs and put Boel on her pot.

"Let's see her!" Some of the girls were curious and came

with me to Boel's room. They stood in the door while Boel sat on her potty chair.

"And she doesn't mind that we look at her? Hello, Boel! What an unusually good-natured child, that she doesn't mind!"

I felt a cold chill in my heart. What now? Boel doing her business, without paying any attention to the door. No one might be there for all she cared.

"She is a little shy," I admitted.

"Quite understandably. Sleepy too, of course."

I stood there and looked at my child: was it shyness, or . . . ?

One of the contralto singers said: "Our little girl would not like anyone to be watching at such a time. She would yell to high heaven, being exposed to a lot of foolish women like this! Let's leave her alone. Good-bye, Boel, good night!"

Boel never looked toward the door as they left. What did it mean? What *did* it mean?

❧

"Why does she make a sound like that?"

We were sitting in the living room, my boss and I, going over a new building research project. From upstairs came Boel's voice, a rhythmically singing tune, a monotonous conglomeration of sounds, repeated over and over. Always the same. I was familiar with that song, rather cute, I thought. Perhaps a little monotonous, sometimes higher pitched, sometimes lower in intensity.

"Does she always sing like that?"

"Do you think it sounds different from what it should?" I said, at once becoming confused. "What is wrong with her little song that I haven't noticed?"

"It only struck me as funny," he said. "Perhaps she is musical."

"Does it disturb you in some way?" I asked, and suddenly I felt that the little piece was very penetrating; it could be heard throughout the house.

"No, of course, it doesn't disturb me," he assured me. "Forget it. It was only I had never heard anything like that from a baby before."

"She is not much for flirting, is she?"

Boel and I had gone down to Valdemarsvik to visit friends. We mothers were sitting in the garden; we had put the children's playpens in the sun, and now we were comparing notes.

In one pen stood a little boy, somewhat bowlegged, pulling and shaking the slats, tumbling over on the mattress, bubbling at the mouth, jabbing, spitting, noisily. Now he was angry. He stuck his little hands between the slats, grabbed the next pen, pulled its slats in impotent fury, found no satisfaction in his desire for community play and finally made faces.

In the next pen sat Boel. She didn't look at the boy, her eyes were turned elsewhere. She sat and rocked back and forth, rhythmically, self-obsessed. The sun played in her light hair which now definitely promised to become curly. Monotonous tunes came from her mouth, I recognized the melody— the same as before.

A toy landed in Boel's pen. But it remained untouched at her side. Next came a little wooden truck, equally unnoticed. Only the little song indicated that Boel still was awake, in spite of all. And her rocking motion continued, of course.

The boy at last became furious, and there was danger that he might turn over his pen. We laughed heartily—it was just too comical.

"Well, well, she is different from most girls nowadays. She won't have any trouble keeping the boys in line! She is not an ordinary girl if she can remain indifferent like that!"

The boy was by now so desperate from the failure of his overtures that we had to pick him up and comfort him. We had hoped for a quiet chat, the two of us mothers, but nothing would do—he kicked and screamed, and we finally had to carry in his pen. Not until his older brothers entered into the game and comforted him did he quiet down.

But out in the garden, in the sun, Boel was sitting alone. Still rocking. Still singing her tune.

III

Now the spying began in earnest; a kind of secret watching. It followed along certain definite lines.

It is a cruel word: to spy. No pleasant associations. Yet, I can find no better expression for what gradually came to take place around Boel—at her bed, her playpen, outside her door. I had begun to observe her constantly. I didn't know exactly why. It was a sort of sly hunt for symptoms, of what I didn't know.

Many of our aquaintances had new babies in their families at about the same time Boel was born. I began to compare. I recalled again and again how it was when our two older children were at her age. They were "early," as our expression was. Neighbors and friends had often told us so: Well, really, can he already sit! Isn't that unusual? My own, she still lies there like a little bun. Or: Does she already keep herself dry? Isn't she a most clever one! My children were much slower.

Now it was my turn to make such comparisons. I did it very quietly and said little about it. But in my heart a picture took form, not clear and comprehensive; rather like a puzzle that had to be considered for a long time before the mysterious lines made a picture. Or like those white sheets of paper one had to rub with the wrong end of a pencil until a recognizable picture appeared. Boel's puzzle-picture had not yet appeared, her sheet was still white, without lines. Was it also—empty?

During the nights I would be at her door, listen, perhaps open it a little, check her breathing. It sounded like most children's when they are asleep.

It happened that I stole up to her bed, stood there and watched, bent over her and—looked for something. I did not find it. I did not even know what signs I was looking for.

I wheeled her around in the perambulator, talked baby talk to her, waved to her, sometimes at a run, or stopping quickly, pulling and pushing joltingly as one does when trying to amuse little children. She sat calmly with her head back, her eyes somewhere up among the pale blue autumn skies. I had a feeling that she had no time for me and my silly nonsense.

Her weight increased according to the chart. Her color was good; dimples had now appeared in the usual places—at her knees, elbows, along her little knuckles. She was beginning to pull herself up to a standing position. This even seemed premature. I simply had no reason to take her to a doctor.

But anyway, one day I was there.

It was a cool fall day; Boel was ten months old. It was our usual children's doctor, emanating calm security, a sure guarantee that nothing evil would befall his little patients. He is a born pediatrician, one could not imagine him in any other capacity.

I had come to ask him the question—it would have to be broached sooner or later—I felt I had the courage with him:

"Tell me, Doctor, I wonder if there is anything wrong with her hearing? Or her eyes? Or is this little girl of ours—is there anything wrong with her brain?"

Now it was said. The doctor seemed startled; he busied himself with the stethoscope while he asked:

"What reason have you to think so, Mrs. Junker?"

"I don't know. I don't think she . . . it seems she doesn't react when one speaks to her. Not like the others. I don't know. . . ."

The doctor made his examination according to the rules. He left nothing untried; he put his hand on her skull and pressed it gently against the great fontanel; he listened to her heart; he felt her joints, checked the reflexes, the Babinski, the patellar, and whatever they are called. There was nothing he missed.

I was beginning to feel reassured, little suspecting how fallacious it was.

❧

Those doctors.

What would we do if we didn't have them to hang on to? To blame when our arguments end?

They have chosen their profession by themselves; they must know when we come that this is no question of a little baby only. They must know that the patients are two. At least two. They have chosen their profession, and this must be an elementary part of their training.

They must know that one day we shall say: "The doctor said . . . this, or this, or that." They have never asked for their share of the guilt. But they get it. Entirely gratis. As an extra bonus to their fee. Not everybody receives such an extra bonus—a quite tax-free addition to the bill.

Each doctor is a new delay. Each word from his mouth carries something new with it—something of eternal future.

The world would be emptier if he weren't there, the doctor. To be blamed. His report is seldom clear or definite, as one might have anticipated. How could it be, when nothing is clear and definite? But what he says is clothed in a mysterious fairy-tale dress—the chasing riddle of the verbal symbol. Encephalitis. Only one example. That word has a beautiful rhythm. Like aphasia, audimutitas, mongoloid, cerebral palsy.

And autism, the most beautiful of them all. Lovely verbal fancy-dresses for the indisputable fact.

The doctor knows little about what type of role he is destined to play. For many, many years to come he must play that role, he must stay in this or that family and become the one they have to depend on. He might well have refused the role if he had foreseen its full meaning in the beginning. But he suspects nothing of this, he only mumbles his diagnostic formulas. And we carry them home with us as valuables. Strange objects which one day shall be costly antiquities. Rare finds we take forth to show when there are guests at home.

The word carries its own mystery, ruled by nothing. A spell, one might call it, but that is too simple. The word has its own power which grows and grows.

The doctor said.

We could never survive without this escape. This is perhaps a dubious honor, Doctor. Many of my friends who have taken the Hippocratic oath might object if I told them this to their faces. But they shouldn't. They don't know how many cuts in the wrists they have averted through the magic of their words.

If they knew it they could accept an occasional wrong diagnosis with greater equanimity; because it too carries with it the blessed delay, cheering us, helping us over the ups and downs. A mistake might be more valuable than we imagine—it might lead to future discoveries. Only to know that one day it might be righted gives it golden wings of hope.

A mistake has also another side. It discharges some of our diffuse guilt, this irrational feeling which so many of us harbor without daring to take it out and examine it in daylight.

Such, then, is the doctor's role that he must be the one to share our guilt.

This first doctor did not make a wrong diagnosis. He made no mistake. What he said had its value all the same even if not as hopeful as a mistake. It had its value, as I soon was to find out. He showed Boel his bunch of keys, then he hid them. Then he jingled them lightly behind one of her ears. She turned her head toward the sound. He jingled them behind her other ear. Again she turned her head.

"Well, her hearing is all right!" he said. "Nothing wrong with it as far as I can see!" He held the keys in front of Boel's eyes. She blinked. He moved them up and down, back and forth. She followed with her eyes. "She sees very well too, as far as I can judge from a quick check. Anyway, there's nothing to indicate lack of contact."

"Well—what do you think, then, Doctor?"

"To tell the truth, I don't think anything. It's possible that she seems a little—what shall I say—a little unengaged." He dangled his stethoscope in front of Boel, inviting her to grab hold of the tubes and examine them. "Perhaps she isn't as interested as one might expect. But children are so different. It might be her way."

"What must I do then?"

"My dear Mrs. Junker—your girl is actually well and healthy. In A-1 condition for a baby. I have no advice. We must wait and see what the future brings. She is so little yet, only ten months."

"But there is such a great difference between her and the older children, the way they were when small. She is so serious."

"She doesn't laugh? Is that what you mean, Mrs. Junker?"

"Well, she does laugh. But not very often."

"Does she laugh at the right time—if you understand what I mean, Mrs. Junker?"

I remained silent. This was a fundamental question; I didn't as yet suspect how fundamental. In its way it was one of the keenest questions that was to be put to me during the blind pursuit which started that day and was to continue for many years.

It was a vital question.

And I didn't know how to answer.

"It might not be so easy to tell," said the doctor, at length. "Let's wait and see."

As I wheeled Boel homeward I had been given a new

respite. I leaned over the baby carriage—actually I thought she laughed back at me. At the right time?

*

Christmas passed, a new year was beginning. Boel started walking in March, not particularly early for a baby, nor late. Actually, it meant nothing. She walked like all other babies. Should we see a doctor again? What should I say this time?

We have a good friend, originally a friend of my husband from his college days. He has a position at a very modern pediatric hospital. He had helped us before. Would I dare call on him? I had, of course, nothing definite to come with. Besides, he was busy with a book—should I bother him with something so intangible?

I fought with my conscience. But one day I was sitting in his office with my vague apprehensions. I told him about my sly observations. He made a constructive suggestion:

"Why don't you bring her in here and let's examine her in every respect. You'll never get any peace otherwise. We can accept her for 'indication of possible toxoplasmosis.' "

"What in all the world is that?"

"It's a disease our chief has discovered only recently. It's supposed to be rather common among women, and if they get it during pregnancy it might affect the child. Tests must be made from both mother and child. A woman doctor here will take the case history. She'll ask you all that might mean anything. You must repeat to her your observations."

Tests were taken, and one day I was sitting across the desk from the woman doctor who was taking the case history. She asked about father, mother, brothers and sisters, relatives, number of rooms, help or not, apartment or house, separate room for the baby or not, baby sicknesses, breast-fed, first tooth, first steps, first smile. "And which words can she say?"

"Words? None at all. She doesn't say anything."

"Nothing at all? Not even Mamma?"

"I don't believe so. She prattles to herself, but one can't call it words. Rather a kind of song she's humming to herself."

"Well, she is so little yet; one mustn't expect much."

I was becoming rather alarmed at all these questions and wondered what they might mean. The number of rooms? Perhaps . . . perhaps it was a mistake, this, to let Boel have a room all to herself. It was the way we had built our house, thinking of the future; each child was given his or her little cabin, each his door to close for privacy. We had been thinking of the need for undisturbed studies, children's need for privacy with friends. And we had built accordingly. Could this have been a mistake? In our old flat she had never been left to sleep alone in a room. Our house—our effort and pride —had it been wrong in some way?

And suddenly I found myself, greatly agitated, explaining about isolating Boel for two months because Lena had come down with the whooping cough. Could this have caused something? Had Boel been alone too much? There hadn't been the same stimulus to talk. Had the change perhaps been too sudden?

The doctor hardly thought so. She kept talking about the toxoplasmosis, this new thing with the strange name.

It is remarkable, but it actually seems one can get some irrational comfort from a new name to play with. One feels inside that it couldn't be so, rather just something in one's imagination. Yet it is so, and one can neither stop it nor deny it—it is a comfort to have a name one can refer to, whose probabilities one can discuss.

"What then are the probabilities?"

The doctor was unsure; as far as she could see, the prognosis was not promising. It was—at least in most cases, she thought —a progressive illness. I noticed she was hesitant—this woman doctor—and I could understand her; I had myself read up a little on this disease and knew how badly it could end. I did not wish to press her, she had a tenderness that was to be felt. Moreover, why nag about a malady which no one as yet had told us Boel was suffering from? I only wanted momentary comfort in a name, and I could hardly expect her to understand this.

The prognosis was dark, she had hinted. At least it was something.

44

At least there was a prognosis.

❧

The tests were negative.

It was absolutely out of the question that Boel suffered from toxoplasmosis.

And the prognosis? Well, there was no prognosis anymore.

I was sitting in the office of the head doctor of the hospital, and he tried to impress upon me how grateful I must be that the tests had been negative: "I'll tell you exactly how it is, Mrs. Junker," he said. "We are simply unable to find anything wrong with your little girl. That is the whole truth. We've done all we can with the aid of the scientific means at our disposal at this time, and nothing shows up."

"What should I do next, then? Have you anything to suggest?"

The doctor remained silent for a few moments, deep in thought. At last he sighed a little: "Have some more children. That's all I can think of."

"But . . . but how can that help Boel?!"

"Not the child—but you."

Perhaps I was a little astonished at first. Later I have come to realize that this was one doctor fully cognizant of the fact that the patients are two—at least two. This doctor knew much about life, which I myself was not to learn for a long time.

❧

I went to Boel's room to get her and take her home. Our good friend on the hospital staff went with me.

As I reached the door I called to our child. But nothing in her beautiful little face indicated that her mother had come to pick up her dear little girl. She did not reach for my hand; I took hers, was allowed to hold it; she was sweet and good. But the current—that strong, warm flow—was not there. The mother-child current. It was absent. I sought security, escape from this in our friend, in his calm authority. I asked:

45

"Don't you think there is a great difference between her and our other children? Isn't she different? In some way remote?"

"You mustn't forget what an immense variation there is in children," he said. Was it only in my imagination that I felt he was avoiding the real issue—or? "Both the intellectual and the emotional developments progress differently," he continued. "It's quite absurd to insist that all people march in step," he laughed. "Actually, the normal variation is much greater than one is inclined to believe. When children reach school age there might be as much as two years' difference in their development patterns, without being in the least abnormal."

Was his reply meant to delay our worries? Was he trying to save us from something? Was he hiding something—or wasn't he?

I felt it as I left the hospital, this something that was already so familiar to me. On the road we had hitherto wandered—from one doctor's office to another—I had already become intimate with this mood which resembled nothing else.

First came the relief. I could breathe anew, as it were; the air was fresher, cooler. I could face the world with a new courage as I led our little girl by the hand. I met the eye of other mothers, other fathers in open frankness. There was nothing wrong with my child—they hadn't found anything in the hospital. I led a sweet little girl by the hand as all the others did. My step had a new spring.

In the streetcar going home came the second stage, as familiar to me as the first, chasing the relief away; not suddenly, or violently, but creepingly, slowly, yet inexorably: a strange vacuum, a groping among the many questions.

A vacuum with no response.

A new summer had come and with it a new delay. There was, then, nothing wrong with Boel. At least nothing they had been

46

able to pin down. The variation is so great, perhaps up to two years. What can one expect? Surely the day would come with a change. Surely.

But my spying continued. I was unable to stop it.

And now several questions had been added.

"Doesn't she say *anything*? How strange. How old is she actually? Well, perhaps later then. Hello, Boel! Why doesn't she respond when you greet her? Is she afraid of strangers? Is she always so shy? Why does she hide back in the corner?"

Questions. Questions.

A wall grew up slowly, unnoticed, the defense wall around the child, round father and mother, round the family. We went down to the seashore, the three children and I. Close by lived a childhood friend of mine, and she generously offered the children her beach to play on, so we mothers could visit, for we hadn't seen each other for some time. Laughingly she showed off her youngest little girl, still in the diaper stage, with golden curls and dimples in her cheeks.

"It's your fault!" she teased me. "I remember when Boel was born and I visited you. I said to myself: I've got to have a baby like that! They're so wonderful to play with. I remember how excited I was. And here you see the result—isn't she a darling!"

She was a darling. She was as beautiful as Boel. But the eyes of this girl were with us, with her mother, followed us, followed all who came. Prattling, burbling, crying in fury, she crept about on the beach. Everything landed in her mouth, everything must be felt, tasted.

Meanwhile, Boel wandered about near the forest edge, alone with the blueberries and her usual monotonous song. Boel put nothing in her mouth; she did not smear herself with sand and dirt. She picked up a piece of glass from the ground, ran a short distance, found another piece and wandered on.

She carried the bits of glass in her hand, but she didn't cut herself. She did not see us, but she could see the small pieces of glass among the blueberry bushes.

And she kept humming her melody, the same as always.

47

Autumn brought a new project.

Something unusual was being planned: our country was to be host to an international audiology conference. The world's foremost men in the field of sound, speech, and hearing were to consider their latest discoveries in our capital. A thought began to form in my mind.

There was now so much to be read about aberrations in deaf or hard of hearing children, the isolation of the deaf, about the possibilities of its penetration. Perhaps at last? The possibility at least was there. Boel did not hear when called. Was she deaf? Last summer, at the seaside, she had run away several times. We had run hither and yon calling her, but she had never answered, never stopped when called to. And we had commented among ourselves: she doesn't seem to hear when we call her.

Suddenly I had before me the picture of the Inconvenient One at the pension. Was this Fate? Retribution for the loathing I had shown at that time? I had rejected a human being who needed me. I had shooed away a repulsive fly from my presence. A fly that annoyed me. A blowfly that could have bitten me if given the chance. Had I, after all, been bitten?

Thou shalt not forget! This might well have been one of the ten commandments. Thou shalt not forget! Even as a little girl I was often reprimanded because I was so forgetful.

The Inconvenient One I had forgotten, even while he still was near me. Even before anything had happened to be forgotten I had relegated him to oblivion.

Now he had suddenly appeared again.

And once again I was sitting in a doctor's office. This time he was one of my own childhood friends; he had chosen his prominent father's profession, specializing in ear diseases. Our friendship had lasted over the years. His father had been next in importance to my mother's brother, now dead, but once the foremost ear specialist in the capital. We had many ties from our childhood to which I now might hang my newest hope.

"Do you think there might be a possibility that she is deaf?"

He tested with his tuning fork against her skull, he tested with a cow bell behind her back, with a whistle, a drum, and other sound-producing instruments of which he had many.

"There is a rather diffuse reaction," he said, at length, his eyes following Boel questioningly as she wandered off as far from us as possible.

"Does she remind you of deaf children?" I was conscious of the pleading tone in my voice, my desire for something definite, something with a name.

"I'll tell you what!" he said, with a sudden enthusiasm in his voice. "There is one man who knows more of these things than anyone else here. He himself has a son who is deaf. Originally he was a dentist—he knows more about this than I do."

I know what I thought: a dentist? What can he know? How can I go to a dentist in a case like this? I felt a hesitation which I did not want to show to my childhood friend. I had a maxim from my own childhood, a rule formed by my father. He had wanted to study medicine, had done all his preparatory work when his illness cut short his possibilities in that direction. But his illness had done something else to Father; during his travels over the Continent, even as far as North Africa, for a remedy against his aching joints, he followed one principle, a principle he had implanted in me:

Only a specialist knows the answer. Only the best specialist! My father had so many times repeated this thesis that unconsciously I hesitated at the word dentist.

"A dentist?" I said. "What could he . . . ?"

"I advise you to see him," said my friend. "He is not only a dentist, he has recently become an M.D. He knows more than I do. He has had experience in cases like this. I haven't."

But. My "but" was still there. A dentist only recently become an M.D. It took years to become a specialist and all that that magic word encompassed.

"Is that all you can suggest?" I said, doubtfully.

"Well—we have started something along that line here at our hospital," he said. "Two of my colleagues have been to

America, and they are conducting a certain type of audiometer-tests with children. It might be worthwhile—would you like for us to test her hearing by this method?"

"Thank you for your kindness in offering to help me. I'm sure I would feel better afterward. What is an audiometer?"

He gave me a little lecture. For the first time I heard the term "skin-resistance." This sounded logical. Conditioning of reflexes—again the power of words. Again a name to pin one's hope to. Push a button and a solution turns up. Well, why not?

My friend suddenly looked relieved; he had discovered a word on which to hang his comfort at last, even he. A word for another delay, and which exonerated him from the responsibility, so heavy, heavy. A colleague of his would perform the miracle.

So now Boel was again in a hospital.

I'll never forget the day I brought her home. That particular department had not yet fully adapted itself to the new methods; later they would learn the practical limitations of American optimism; by and by the impressive apparatus with the magic name—the PGSR Audiometer—the psycho-galvanic-skin-resistance-audiometer in full—would be pushed aside, put into a closet or somewhere. It could not be used for the unknown forces, the big question marks.

Boel, in her blue bathrobe, was sitting in the hospital hall—she could hardly have been further removed from "the little nursery" where other "cases" lay for examination. She could never have been more absent. I called to her. She kept banging her head against the wall behind her; from the corner of my eye I could see the other children in the nursery, busy at their buildings.

"Boel! Boel! It's Mother!"

Clunk! Clunk! Clunk!—Other children playing together—Boel clunking her head.

The doctor—a new one again, one of those who had been to America—explained the tests to me. Undoubtedly there was something to them. I was reminded of my last year in high school when we read about Pavlov's experiments with dogs—conditioned reflexes. Tests convince those who wish to believe, wish to be persuaded.

The doctor need not say much; I was anxious to believe.

"We have not been able to obtain reaction for less than 80 decibels," he said. "We cannot say if it means she is deaf, but it does mean that she might be. She does not react to sounds."

Yes, I understood.

I wanted to understand. I tried with utmost eagerness to make myself familiar with this intensity measure, the decibel. With the frequency measure, cycles per second, or waves if you wish. I rushed with tense nerves into the audiogram-conception, normal hearing limitations, vibration-senses, and whatever it now is called.

With my child struggling to get out of my arms, I stopped the taxi at a bookstore and ordered books, books: Hallowell Davies: *Hearing and Deafness*; Myklebust: *My Deaf Child*; Lassman: *Language for the Preschool Deaf Child*; Gesell: *Developmental Diagnosis*, and many more. I felt rich with my harvest.

Rich!

There was so much in those books. Usually there is much to be read in books. On one page I even read something about the deaf child's way of stimulating itself by banging its head against something hard. Well, well. I swallowed, and I was rich. Too much that fitted. It was so, exactly so, yes, precisely. Well....

I was rich and I had much to talk about.

Too much.

How long did the miracle last? The dream of something to hold on to? I no longer remember; in dreams time is shorter or longer according to need. I no longer remember my periods of grace; I only remember the gloomy doubt ever present at Boel's bed when I watched her sleep. I remember my silent talks with a sleeping child: You might . . . perhaps you could be . . . well, why not?

My childhood friend with the tender hands for ear passages and cavities, he understood my gloomy doubts. The audiology-congress was just going on; his father, the great prominent physician, had been the initiator; the world's greatest scientists were in our city.

He suggested something remarkable—all of his own—without consideration or hesitation about trouble and inconvenience. He would arrange for me to meet one of the greatest of the world's otologists. A specialist above specialists in audiology. Such a man would know.

I had not been to the prominent physician's home since I was a child, when my uncle was still alive, and all we children played around the Christmas tree; or had our teen-age balls there. I recognized vaguely the tall, solid bookcases, the deeply red Oriental rugs, the gracile ornaments decorating an East Indian vase. The mild voice from the great prominent physician, together with his friendly indifferent smile, came to me from a dark corner of his room, where he sat in his chair almighty and dominating in his white authority. In front of me was one of the world's most famous otology specialists, and his kind eyes left me and wandered to Boel on my knee, and back again. His American voice was distinct and cultivated.

"Does she play with dolls?" he asked.

"No, she likes only hard toys."

"If you give her a bed and a doll, she doesn't try to make the bed and place the doll in it?"

"She throws the doll as far away as possible."

"Does she like animals?"

"Not if they are soft. She only likes hard objects."

"Does she like her mother?"

"I don't know."

"Her father?"

"I don't know."

"Is she jealous of her brother and sister? Or does she like them?"

Boel jealous? I didn't even know if Boel had noticed that she had a brother and a sister. I only knew that they never were jealous of Boel. Nothing of what I had feared in that respect had happened. I remembered Sten playing with a little girl with golden curls but no response. I remembered Lena's tenderness when she pretended mother-and-child with her. Jealousy had no place in those recollections.

All I had felt was my own pain at the other children's attempts, at my husband's tries at contact, at the failure of grandparents and other relatives. All had been stifled, all attempts somehow poor and futile. I had to find some of this and hand it over to this great American in front of me. I tried to find a general characteristic, some expression for this riddle.

Questions and answers shot back and forth between the considerate American with the kind, searching eyes, and this mother who wanted to give an impression of being well supplied with symptoms to prove her ability to observe. I had let Boel down on the floor—the kind American professor wanted to see how she acted when left to her own devices; and our questions and answers, now *sotto voce*, flew back and forth, while Boel took off on her usual wanderings.

She followed along the bookshelves, her fingernails scratching the bindings which prompted me to cry out to stop her, but the host magnanimously urged me to let her be: "Let's observe what she's up to. Please, Karin, don't interfere!"

With my heart in my throat I saw her approach the East Indian vases! "Please, Karin, don't worry. She'll do all right."

Nothing happened to the valuable vases, indeed, nothing at all happened. Boel was a butterfly, fluttering in its streak of mild sunlight, light as a butterfly and as fleeting, touching nothing, hurting nothing, not as would be expected from a two-year-old's clumsiness. Now the little sound-prattle could be heard from her lips as she wandered in and out of the sun streak, further and further removed from us.

"What is she singing?"

There was a new interest in the otologist's voice. I replied: "Always the same tune, always the same tone of voice."

"No variations? No definite melody?"

"Never."

The atonality of her song was unquestionable. He nodded:

53

"Nothing she has heard then? Nothing you've taught her?"

"Oh, no!" I assured him, suddenly aware of the connection, the dreadful relationship. "She has always mumbled like that."

The otologist sighed: "Her toys, those hard ones, does she build anything with them?"

I could see Boel in my mind's eye, a small piece of wood in her hand; the same piece in the evening as in the morning; or some piece of metal, or a piece of cardboard. Hour after hour, the same little hand around the same piece of material, sometimes waving her hand with it, sometimes balancing it. I could see her return to the same object, the same place—like a pendulum, from object to place, from place to object, back and forth, back and forth.

I tried to explain.

"A certain type of deaf children have a tendency to perseverate," said the American doctor. "It's quite typical, this perseveration."

I recalled the books I had read; the word was there. *Perseveration*—to hold on, physically and mentally, to happenings or objects. It could be some sort of lacking will, or perhaps, on the contrary, too strong a will to hold on. Typical of many. Typical for both the deaf and non-deaf.

The American expert continued his examination with a minuteness and a patience that gave me a bad conscience. I felt like interrupting him with: Save your valuable time! Spend it on someone who needs it more!—I don't know why I suddenly felt sorry for him, this rather concerned stranger who devoted so much time and effort to my little girl, in this house of childhood memories, all the while observed by the prominent physician who gently tapped his fingers as he sat in his chair back in the corner.

"Well," said the American at last, "I think your child is very, very deaf. She seems to have no hearing at all. Of course, she is still so little—a definite diagnosis is impossible—but that is my belief. Thank you so much for bringing her to me— it has been a great pleasure to meet your sweet little girl. Very, very interesting. But, please, don't worry now; true, it isn't easy with a deaf child, but you can do a great deal to help her.

And your Swedish doctors can give you advice and help. You must read. . . ."

The books he mentioned I already had. The American friendliness, in many ways alien to our country's stiffness, so warming in its unalterable belief in given patterns, gave me new air, a new breathing spell. Perhaps the spell was fragile, but at least he had given me something, the value of which I only later was able to analyze. I had been given something definite.

After all, there is something to this, to have consulted one of the world's foremost doctors, to be able to discuss his opinions with other great specialists. From being a small riddle in an empty room with walls of questions Boel had taken the step of becoming a possibly deaf child, an interesting case. This step was not conclusive—but it was a step.

The sun played in her flaxen locks, caught her, seemed to follow her as she ran along meeting all the strolling people on the street as we wandered homeward, her blue skirt fluttering around her chubby limbs.

IV

Hardly a week after my interview with the American guest of the prominent physician the doubts again assailed me, stealing out of their corners as it were; their sharp-edged whispers popped up in every attempt to discuss the situation with others, in every fumbling, desperate attempt to follow the instructions in the books.

In the beginning I refused to air these doubts; I stifled them under the diagnosis "probably very, very deaf." This had its magic. Deep within me I knew, however, that it wasn't definitive; in the same sense that nothing is definitive for those of us who struggle with this fate. Nothing except death is definite. No, the magic diagnosis, after all, had been anything but definitive. On the contrary, the American had said quite clearly that he was unable to give a definitive opinion.

He had only expressed a supposition, and referred to books which offered a program of training for deaf children and advice about their upbringing. That was all. But his supposition had opened a door ever so little, a door to the future.

Then again doubt stood hidden behind this door—a few months later to push the door wide open. By then we had reached another spring.

Three years ago a friend and I had spent Easter together at Klövsjö. At that time she and I had been pregnant. Now our respective children were about two and a half years old, and it was long since I had had an opportunity to compare. At least since I had had this closer and more obvious opportunity offered by children of intimate friends. The opportunity came with this invitation to have a spring dinner together. We were still noisily greeting each other in the hall, reviving our "pregnancy jokes," when someone called loudly from an inside room: "Mummy, Mummy! Come and say good night! Mummy, come quick!"

A young voice was demanding attention in the nursery.

"Want to come and help me tuck in Bure?" my friend suggested. "He doesn't settle down until I've said good night formally."

I stood transfixed for a moment. At first I hadn't realized that a little child had called for Mother, a little child that lay in its mother's womb at the time I was expecting Boel. Now it was as if lightning had struck me.

"Mummy! Mummy! Hurry up! Come!" the boy was calling.

Half-numb I walked behind her into the nursery. A two-year-old was sitting upright in his bed, with teasing insistence complaining about his delayed prayer and sleep-kiss. My arms felt heavy as lead.

I stood nailed to the spot as the baby jumped from his bed, hung around his mother's neck, listened to her night-comfort prattle of her good-boy-jump-into-bed-now.

This realization I had not experienced before. Where had my eyes been, how could I so have forgotten to observe? How could I have forgotten that children of that age are busy with teddy bears that comfort, ask for a night-pot within reach, can pull blankets and sheet over their shoulder, with a pillow in their arms?

Thou shalt not forget!

But I had forgotten. Forgotten that a child of two clings to its mother's neck, never to let go, clings hard with jealousy's will of possession. That it complains and cries when Mother has company, invents endless excuses to keep her close. They are thirsty, need go to the bathroom, are cold, perspire, are thirsty again, want a drink, want the lights on, want them off, want the door open, want it closed.

No, they do not repel Mother when she bends over them—they try to keep her with them with endless inventions. They hold firmly, restively, and their tricks are many.

I stole out of the nursery as I whispered: "You'll have better luck quieting him if I leave. See you later."

Out in the hall I stumbled toward the living room door, heard the noisy, happy voices in there. Slowly I turned and went into the bathroom. I closed the door and leaned against the white, cold tile wall, paralyzed. Tears dropped from my eyes onto the facing of my new, blue moiré suit, forming round salt stains, certainly impossible to remove. Not even the strongest cleaning fluid would ever obliterate them.

Assuredly, the respite granted by the American had brought a certain easement; for a few months I had had something to talk about, some prognosis to speculate about. And I had been entirely ready to accept delayed mental development as a natural result of deafness. Both delayed and dwarfed . . . but . . . .

This difference. Was it really so great—between the deaf child and the hearing one? Had Boel taken that certain step, or hadn't she? The step from no-man's-land of questions to the more secure ground of the deaf-diagnosis?

This difference. There must be something more to explain. In the last few months I had read a great deal about deafness, about the importance of speech for human contact. But I had not been willing to open that door which stood ajar. Subconsciously I had shied away from seeing it wide open.

Now the door was open. Now someone appeared again,

someone from the past, on the path to the swimming hole on a balmy late-summer day. I was beginning to recognize him, the Inconvenient One. Now he appeared again, talked, argued. And his voice came so clear I could actually hear it: "Had I no feelingsh you sshhay?"

I had nothing to answer. I was conscious of my guilt, wanted to redress it, but as yet I didn't know how.

❧

Now a new period began; a period that would be hectic. As yet I knew nothing of all the incidents and connections which would eventually shape my pattern into a kind of harmony; and now, afterward, I do not wish to impute the burden of a fateful future on happenings which they did not have. I'll only tell the story, and the words may indicate the future as they will.

This was the fortieth anniversary of the Swedish Scout Movement. Agreement had been reached to celebrate differently this time—to give instead of receive gifts. The idea was that healthy, normal children would give to some group of the handicapped children.

When it finally was decided that the forty-year-gift was to go to deaf children and children with defective hearing, I already knew the truth—we both knew the falseness of the last diagnosis; this drive for deaf and hard of hearing children had nothing to do with our child. Nothing more than perhaps starting this thing. An American had suggested something about deafness; perhaps because of that Boel had been selected to indicate a group in need of aid who would receive it.

She had perhaps indirectly shown the way, but already she herself stood by the side of the road, and the ditch was broad and deep. Meanwhile another spring blossomed over the meadows, so silent and empty to her. A new spring, with its febrile preparations for the coming celebration, was to steal away from us—as had happened so often before—robbing us of the few, fleeting spring evenings, so filled with blue-glittering skies and songs of returning birds that only a Stockholm spring can offer.

59

And yet—it was one of these very song-filled, twilight evenings that was to awaken an impulse in me, a pointing finger as it were. I was standing on the stoop of our cottage when the clear *cantilena* of the blackbird reached me from our neighbor's spruce. I walked out into the graveled yard—a light rain had fallen and with it brought down a carpet of white petals from our cherry tree on the hill. The gravel crackled underfoot, distant voices were calling to each other down at the shore, and the first spring trial of the outboard motor was going on. Sounds. The sounds of spring against a crimson sunset between scattering rain clouds.

Were Boel deaf these things would not exist. Now Boel can hear perhaps. Yet, these things do not exist for her. To hear, then, is not only to receive sounds with the hearing apparatus. There is a connection, perhaps several, that must function to give the sounds meaning, reception, and interpretation. I myself, apparently, have not been hearing in the proper way; I have only accepted hearing as a natural function without special mood-values.

This day something was awakened within me which by and by would grow to assume a rapacious life interest; an eluding riddle taunting me as I pursue it. Will I ever find its solution?

My next medical step was to be taken in the pursuit of this riddle. The prominent physician has numerous relatives serving in the healing profession. Especially one of his famous relatives—a professor at the university-hospital where Boel was born—has devoted his life to research in audiology, a name covering the conglomeration of diseases and discoveries in the field of hearing—medical, psychological, pedagogic, acoustical, technical.

Sitting in the office of this doctor—Boel as usual running away to the farthest corner—both he and I knew, I felt, that we needn't speak of deafness or hearing. I no longer remember if he even looked in Boel's ears. No, such a simple trick he didn't engage in, and now it struck me that this trick—which the American had used—perhaps is part of some American parent-treatment-routine. Now, afterward, I willingly forgive him; we all have to have our symbol-actions. Yet, it

60

pleased me that this Swedish otologist showed sufficient consideration for me to let Boel keep busy in her corner. Busy with nothing.

We spoke of many things, perhaps mostly of the possibilities of starting preschools for hard of hearing children through the Scout Movement. He spoke with warmth and enthusiasm about the dentist who had become a medical doctor, and whom I had not yet had the courage to visit. He told me of this man's method, by speaking directly into the ear trying to activate the vague hearing prevalent with most deaf children; in this way awaken a consciousness of speech the natural way, through the ear.

I think we both felt my visit was futile. As a medical visit it was doomed in advance. What is it, then, that drives one on, from one highly polished M.D. sign to another?

We must do something, undertake something, to cover up our poverty. We must have something to indemnify our obligation when the creditor comes and demands payment. The means of payment is the same for most of us: I have been to that doctor, and that one, and that one. I have run around and tried and tried. Everything.

I was sitting with that otologist knowing I was demanding much and having little to pay with. Yet, I had come to him. As if. I was a narcotic victim with only three choices—to increase the dose, increase its frequency, or with resignation admit the declining effect of the drug; a narcotic addict longing for relief, if ever so little. It is easy to sink so low. The only counterweight I had to support my self-respect was my growing understanding.

In the usual order we went through the usual questions; in spite of all, an interview is as rule-bound as a football game or any other game. Each sentence, each word depends on how one's opponent receives it. One doesn't decide the rhythm, this is decided by the rules of the game. And one's thoughts easily get out of rhythm if one doesn't follow the rules. The rules in our game were that deep within us we both knew we weren't talking about that which actually existed.

61

And yet, this doctor-call was to be different from most of the others. The definite word wasn't said this time either, but this doctor did not for a moment forget the third rule of the medical profession: *toujours consoler*, always comfort. He had a new outlook, a fine feeling for the comforting qualities of diversion. In our game of words he cleverly threw his ball into the neutral field of children with hearing loss.

"Nurse!" he presently called out. "Oh, Nurse—I think we had better call and find out. . . ." By now he was in the other room, mumbling low-voiced instructions to his office nurse. Then he came back: "We're calling a mother who has two deaf children to see if she's home. Then you must take Boel with you and go and see her."

"But why?"

"I think it would be good for you to meet her," he said. "She's working hard with her children, using that new method of auditory training. I believe she can help you."

"But Boel is hardly. . . ."

"I think it would be good if you had a talk with her."

It was good that I did talk with her.

During the years that have passed since I first called on her, I have met so many tense mothers, so many "maimed" families. I know what the slick surface means. I have learned to recognize the fisted hands that should have been delicate women's hands but have turned into hard workingmen's hands —without the expected roughness. I know the tense surface is strong, but it isn't so elastic and soft as other surfaces. And when it bursts then it bursts with a vengeance. But—her surface held.

It was good that I went. She was the first one, and her struggle one of the greatest. She was beautiful, and strong as a young pine from the Värmland forest, her faith could move mountains. Her faith indeed almost unbalanced my disbelief.

She yelled into her boy's ear: "Good morning, Mrs. Junker!"

"Good morning, Miss Unker," repeated the boy, seriously staccato.

She lifted her little girl toward the chandelier until the

crystals jingled among the blond curls: "Lamp! Lam-m-p!"
Her voice, so soft and low in our conversation, trumpeted
artlessly until her neck arteries were tight as wash lines from
the effort.

The girl was silent.

"Lamp! Lamp! Lamp!"

The girl laughed dizzily but kept her silence.

"I might have to say lamp a thousand times before she repeats it. I have said every word Gunnar knows thousands of
times. I know she too will say lamp at last. It's only to keep
at it. She'll do it, I know."

She was saved—but I was outside the Portals of Grace with
my doubts. In an instant she had Boel on her knee. She
pushed a wooden truck across the living room table: "Caaar!
Car! Caaaar!"

Boel did not watch the car, she turned her head as far
away as she could from the penetrating voice.

"Train! Traaain!" Now it was a little metal train that was
rolling over the table top. "Train! Traaain!"

But Boel broke loose and ran to the corner. Suddenly she
started her little melody; a little differently, perhaps; one
might discern vowels and consonants.

"Listen! Listen!" this beautiful Värmland Pine cried enthusiastically. "Didn't you hear her say train actually?"

Then she was after Boel, crawling behind her across the
floor: "Train, train, train!" her mouth following Boel's ear:
"Train! Train!"

The train also crawled across the floor. Boel stopped,
looked startled. Did she look at the train? Her eyes wandered
away; she was back at her old melody.

The proud Värmland Pine rose from the floor, pushed her
hair back from her forehead; her beautiful eyes glittered, she
was a young woman—and an ancient mother at the same time.
She had a healthy strength that pushed me up against the wall.
She kept talking, talking for a long, long time. Her road led
only in one direction—straight forward. No crooked bypaths.

"She did say train! I believe she hears better than my children. Isn't it amazing that I could make her say train?"

After a long visit I had to leave. With Boel holding my hand we tramped down the three flights of imitation marble steps (no elevator), steps that would become familiar to me over the years.

Something of the strength of this pine was now in me; yet all the time I was conscious of my distance from Boel. I had made my decision. My road was not staked out by someone who knew the answer; I myself must seek it. As if. Through a wild and dark forest a narrow path is better than no path at all.

I would feed Boel with words and speech—as if. I would follow the patterns and schemes that were available. No one would ever be able to say that I hadn't tried.

With Boel on my knee I grew warm from excitement in the streetcar as I pointed to the cars that drove by, and using her sweet ear as a funnel repeated, over and over: "Car! Car!"

Many of the passengers watched.

During the following three years I was to stick to that pattern. I knew its narrow limits, but I followed it because, at least, it was a path through the dark, if ever so narrow. Even though I was thoroughly convinced that the path led in the wrong direction, to a place where Boel did not belong, I still kept walking, because my walk was a motion, an action. Not passive, expectant waiting.

The motion became my life's tenet. I cannot tell how many times I must have repeated, my mouth at Boel's ear, my diction clear: "Give me your foot, Boel! The other foot! Hands up! Bath, Boel! Come, Boel! The train, the car, the lamp. Mother, train, lamp, mother! Traaain! Laaaamp!"

It is now ten years later. Boel does not yet say train.

I get ahead of myself. The measure is not yet full. For a heaped measure much remains; there is still much to tell.

"Sleep, sleep, baby mine. A princess walks in the forest, with golden hair, with crown and silver buckles. . . ."

I was coming across the mountain meadow and could hear my son singing in our cottage: "Soon Father will come and take the Princess in his sack, home to his little Dumpe. . . ."

It was August, and we had gone to Klövsjö in the mountains, the three of us—Sten, Boel, and I. I opened the door, and Sten, my "Dumpe" son was singing his song to Boel. He hid Boel under the blanket on his bed, took the "Princess" in his sack, and Boel laughed, laughed in her sack. "We'll put her in a golden cage, and keep watch o'er our golden Princess. . . ." Now Boel was taken out of the sack and put in big brother's golden cage, his arms the grill of the cage, his fingers the golden bars. Now she flies up in the air, now in dizzy speed toward the floor, toward the ceiling, and down again.

"She'll jump and dance on her toes . . .
Chirrup and sing like birds in the bush . . . ."

Boel was rushing in wild flight from one corner of the room to the other, laughing to her heart's content. Sten was clapping his hands in rhythm with her motions. It was late in the evening, Sten was trying to tire Boel so we all could get some sleep.

But Boel kept right on, "jumping and dancing on her toes, chirrupping and singing like the birds in the bush." For Boel was not tired.

She never got tired.

Ends of yarn—red, yellow, blue. I started with red, that was easiest. I tied together red and red, yellow and yellow, blue and blue. Boel was given a piece of yarn, and I showed her what to do. Boel picked up her yarn, ran to her corner where she let it dangle from her left hand while she slowly hit it with her right to make it swing like a pendulum. She busied herself with this single yarn exclusively, ignoring the other colors.

Marbles of the same colors, same demonstration. Boel would pick up one marble, drop it as if it had burned her, run to her corner, and refuse to touch it again. Then she began to look for the yarn and complained.

Instead of colors I tried with objects of the same shape.

Two and two. Two spoons, two knives, two forks. I gave the spoon to Boel—it said in the book that this was the easiest. Easiest to classify. I showed her and waited. And waited again.

Boel threw away the spoon and ran to her corner and started to yell. She did not want to classify, she wanted her yarn to hit.

We went out on the stoop of our mountain chalet, and now I tried with cut-out pictures. One husky little baby would sit upright and advertise porridge, a diaper round his full belly, a hearty, dimpled smile on his happy face.

I showed her the picture; I had others behind my back. "Baby! Baaaby! Baby!"

Boel ran to her corner, yelling. The picture was no baby, it was a piece of paper to be hit until it dangled between my fingers. And the yarn was lost.

We went to the upper meadow to fetch our evening milk. The women who spend their summers there had been my friends over the years. I showed them my little demonstration, they became interested and wanted to help. They talked to Boel as *if*. Marta showed a picture on the wall; she was excited and wanted immediate result.

"A chicken!" she said. It was an Easter picture which had been left there. "Chicken! Rooster! Chicken!"

She lifted Boel to the picture, repeated her chicken-and-rooster. Lella tried with a cow; she held Boel to a pastoral scene on the chalet wall.

"Cow, cow, mooooh!"

And Olga had a horse called Polle. Now Polle is a good word for hard of hearing children, a word with a great many low frequencies. Exactly the kind of word the dentist who became an M.D. would like to use. And the pictures were good. Exactly like the American books expected them to be. Simple, direct, natural. Good for training exercises.

But Boel kept to her corner.

"Isn't there some sort of operation for this?" suggested Olga. "It might help. Hoppla, Polle! Listen, Boel! Hoppla, Polle! You wait and see—she'll grow out of it!"

They wouldn't accept the fact that no remedy existed. They wouldn't admit the invincible. Boel is the child in the glass ball, alone in her world but visible to all.

She walked out in the meadow. We kept talking for perhaps five minutes, and suddenly we realized that Boel was nowhere to be seen. She disappeared quickly and got as far away as possible. If there hadn't been a fence around the meadow she would have been lost in the wilderness in no time. We finally found her, in the farthest corner of the field, up against the fence, banging her back against the juniper wickets until they swayed.

As I walked back to my own chalet, I was grateful to be out in the country. Lidingö, the Stockholm suburb where our home is, is also in the country in a way, and I was pleased that I could let my lone bird out to flap her wings at times. There she could "dance and jump on toe, and chirrup and sing like birds in the bush."

I know this is a grace.

The autumn that followed was unusually long and warm and hectic. September brought an Indian Summer. Our mountain vacation had been a disappointment, a sort of heartache over something that never really had been. School bells were again ringing, streets were bedded in little clouds of dust, the theaters opened. The sun flooded down through the heated maple leaves on our place, as generously as it had done three years ago during my autumn of expectancy. And these September days, too, trembled in expectancy, an undefinable excitement stimulated all of us at the prospect of our undertaking.

In an old-fashioned private flat in Stockholm an intensive auditory training had already been started, as a preliminary to the Forty-Year-Jubilee of the Swedish Boy Scout Movement when we hoped to enlist some fifty thousand children, youths, and grownups in our drive: "The Red Knot, For the Benefit of the Deaf and Hard of Hearing Children!"

A devoted mother, with clear vision and firm confidence, had opened her largest and most attractive room for the purpose. Two women teachers had been engaged, a bold decision before a penny had been collected. But it was important to have something to show on the opening day when the idea of the Red Knot was to be presented to the public. The opening itself would take place in the City Hall, under great fanfare and blow of trumpets, with the King and the royal family present to view the parade of Boy Scouts and their leaders. And at the headquarters preparations were under way for a second preschool to inspire the scouts to more contributions. Daring expectations, one might say.

Later I was to learn that our aim at times was too high. But I am also convinced that one "must aim high to reach half the goal." This autumn, so filled with intense activity, was in some way to change all of us. A milestone is perhaps too big a word, yet. . . .

At long last I met the dentist who became an M.D. because of his deaf son. I think both of us felt that Boel was a bird of another nest; at least I had no illusions. But I had a mechanical pattern to follow, and even this has its value. And the remarkable dentist knew this too; this man who was to become one of the many real friends my strange fate has brought me.

Our first little schoolroom had a glass-pane in the wall of the door of American "one-way" type; one can see through a glass which on the other side is a mirror, so that people in the room do not know anyone is observing them. Through this glass mothers could undisturbed observe and learn the method of auditory training of their children. I myself stood many days behind the glass, together with mothers from all parts of the country. We discussed low-frequency and high-frequency sounds, the importance of the father's participation —if a father there was—and many other matters.

One day I was standing at the window with another mother at my side. In the room were little Kristina, Axelman, and Bettan, sitting on their stools at a round table with interesting picture-combinations. All the children reacted. Alone in a corner Boel fluttered about, outside as usual. Presently one of the teachers spoke up, with a nod of the head toward the corner where Boel sat with indifference: "That little one— she is hopeless!"

It was an innocent, thoughtless remark that had escaped this young woman, and it needs no comment; how could she know that the mother was standing behind the glass. A mother with this pain that constantly burns. No, she couldn't know. I whispered to the mother at my side: "It's my girl she is talking about—the one back there in the corner. . . ."

At last I paid my tribute to an irrational guilty conscience. In the beginning I took Boel downtown on a bicycle to her auditory training school; the use of the streetcar seemed to me an unnecessary torture. In my youth I had enjoyed riding a bicycle, and now I bought a baby seat with a belt for Boel. Why not?

My optimism was premature.

That fall they were rebuilding the high and long Lidingö-bridge that connects our suburb with Stockholm proper. A narrow path for walkers and cyclists was open, and on either side, through beams and trestles, we could look down on the glittering water flowing far, far below us. Only a flimsy hand rail protected us on either side.

When we reached the bridge Boel always began to sway in her seat. I tried to get hold of her hands and make her sit quietly. No, she wanted to sway. I was afraid I might lose my balance and stopped the bicycle and tightened her belt. But Boel enjoyed the swaying and would not hold onto me. I tried to push her small hands under me and sit on them. But she immediately pulled them out. Those glittering waves down there seemed so inviting: Come, come to me!

For three weeks that fall I crossed that bridge twice a day, precariously balancing myself and Boel on the bicycle. (It is part of my story that I have never since used a bicycle.)

My husband's mother and her brother are responsible for making me a car driver, indeed, almost making a second home for me of the car. It was at a dinner in their beautiful flat out at the Gumhornstreet that "Uncle" Gosta with a convivial smile over his cigar looked at me. And since he now is gone—and with him his ever-readiness-to-help—I will tell the story of how I became a servant to the steering wheel for many years.

Some story had been told and all were laughing. But not I. I felt my three weeks cycling in every joint and was no longer able to laugh at stories. Those glittering waves so far below my swaying bicycle were so impressed on my mind that I didn't even get the gist of the story. Presently Uncle Gosta turned to me:

"Karin, you look tired?"

"I *am* tired."

And in the next moment I was telling, simply and art-lessly, everything. I was telling *my* story, without any definite point really; only about a bicycle's precarious passage over a bridge, dizzily high over the water, with no secure protection, and with an unknowing princess dancing in the baby seat.

Uncle Gosta was thoughtfully silent. Not many more stories were told, and we left early. But the following day my mother-in-law called up to say that she and her brother wanted to buy me a car, if cars now were obtainable. They wanted to buy it at once.

Neither one of them owned a car. Neither one of them ever wished to own or learn to drive a car.

This at last gave me an opportunity to do something: they bought a car for me, a car that was to carry many, many deaf children, many, many miles over many, many years, to and from school, in various parts of the city and the suburbs.

Perhaps I will never be able to repay this gift; but I do know one thing: the intimate, daily contact with the little deaf children was to help carry me over much that happened later. It would also create, and ever stimulate, my love for the language, the speech, the word; make me understand its deep function in our lives, appreciate its role.

The Word that was in the Beginning.

During the years that followed I had plenty of time to think of this—at the wheel, with my silent little passengers behind me. Boel hummed and swayed alone in her corner, deep in a world beyond, but I felt now that there was a forgiveness for my playing my pretend-pattern with this little strange bird when we all knew she wasn't deaf. Kristina, Tom, Erik and all the others forgave us, Boel and me.

A car offers a separateness as nothing else. Sociologists in the future will have a rich field when they tackle this group-psychology. How does this new car-group category react?

What a project to be caught in! To investigate all these small worlds that travel side by side, passing each other disdainfully or jealously, in powerful righteousness or only in playful annoyance; these wandering little homes, each with its own atmosphere, its own world of behavior, but all enclosed in the same monotonous, impersonal shell of steel, chrome, and glass. A shell within which only the initiated is able to discern all the small nuances which are making up an unintelligible yet definite group-variation. I had a great deal of time to think, in there in my steel shell.

Kristina, clear-eyed, stood upright back in the car, following everything outside the window, sometimes exploding in a one-syllable comment, the deaf one's flutelike hollowness of voice cutting through the soft humming from the corner. Tom used to roll about proudly in his home-knitted outfit; Erik's brown squirrel-eyes registered every make of car that passed. Speechless, observant silence reached me from the back of the car—and Boel's monotonous humming.

Once when we passed the Palace Guard Kristina acted out and said "soldier-boom-boom." It struck me that the pattern of uniformity is far more esthetically appealing than the pattern of non-uniformity. I wonder why? Has it always been so, or is it that perhaps we only think so, in this age of standardization? No, Gestalt psychology labels things—it is a law that governs us. We accept that law, whether we otherwise believe in *Gestalt* psychology or not. We need only pull one man out of the Palace Guard and give him individuality, let him walk any way he wishes—and look what an esthetic crime we have committed through this non-uniformity!

Is it so with all uniformity? My little passengers in the back, they were all removed from uniformity. They were forced to meet life in that insecure field outside troop-formations—different, apart. None of the three back there could hear the trumpets and the bugles from the street, they could only see the sun's reflexes against the sparkling brass.

And Boel—she could hear both the trumpets and the bugles, but she didn't look out, because to her they were devoid of meaning—both trumpets and bugles.

The esthetics of uniformity was far removed from the minds of my little passengers.

❧

Word that was in the Beginning.

How was it that I who was born with a love for the word, infatuated with its power and strength, was to travel miles and miles of my fleeting years with silence as a passenger? Just I? Traveling with a silence I hadn't asked for—the enemy of thought?

How was it that I who for so many nights had longed for silence from Boel's room was forced to hate this same silence when it was the silence of Kristina or Erik or Tom?

Words became my clay to be formed—with hands that smarted from a persistent, unsatisfied desire. Words were red and yellow and blue on my pallet. My love for words—the dawn of humanity when thoughts took form—suffered in platonic pain during these endless hours at the wheel.

And behind me sat a child with the technical mechanism ready to grasp this wonderful word that was in the beginning. She would have been able to, but some power had denied her the ability. Beside her sat other children, with observing eyes, and a fight for conquest before them, a fight against and for the word. They would never hear Chopin's *C-minor waltz* come to them through the black box that was the car radio; it was a soundless and pitiful gimmick to them, without meaning.

I knew their fight—so recently begun—would be long. And the victory which perhaps might reward their fight would never be complete. It would never encompass the glamor of the *C-minor waltz*, never the song of the chaffinch, never the wind's rustle through a newly leafed birch in early spring.

The paths they would travel would always wind through silent meadows, and the rustle of the wind would be a nothing, nothing more than a passing caress. Nothing more. The leaves would never play their fugues for them, the waves would never pound.

And what is a blackbird in a spring evening?

A clumsy blackbird, hopping about in the graveled yard, without the enticing spring song. A hungry, audacious animal, nothing more.

To me the word was an auger, a chisel, a hammer, scissors, needle, and thread. The tools of night and day. Had they not been available during nights of anguish my mind would have languished, drooping and dank like a withered potato stalk. Without its injection I would have become a pupa, poor in vitamins, dried-up from lack of blood, and pining away.

But now I had the word—as a gift. And so that autumn a fire was kindled in me: my love for the deaf child, and my hate for deafness.

This fire no one has been able to extinguish. I wish its warmth one day would reach even him, the Inconvenient One. And for him I would here like to quote Oscar Levertin's "The Mother Tongue," for him, yes, even more for Gunnar, Kristina, Erik, Tom, Staffan, Per, Hakan, Goran, Kaj, Majbritt, and the wise Elisabeth, all, all. All those who have had a much harder fight against the word and for it than the Inconvenient One.

> Teller of tales, when I was a child,
> The spirit of dreams you awakened,
> Fantaso's reins of purple yarn

The youth at the fire offered,
Songs that were sung with my mother's tongue,
Thoughts that gave play at the table.
Also for me from beginning's time
The world was created by words.

This love I was to experience in all its strength many, many years later when my husband and I were in India. In the school for the deaf at Delhi, where I spent a "monsoon," I felt more than anywhere else the deaf person's universal hunger for the word. That hunger stretches far beyond latitude and longitude, beyond national borders, beyond race and tongue. It is ever alike. It gropes and gropes—and is mocked again. Ever again.

And my tenderness became almost hurting from the outside to the bottom of my heart. Perhaps too sensitive at times. But always an impotent anger against the immense maiming: *not* to have been granted the Word when one is born a human being.

V

In retrospect past events mingle.

Time was busy. Filled by things to do. By people to meet. By thoughts to ponder. Happenings to be told later.

My first meeting with the State Superintendent for Special Education, the lady of the big heart and the long nose, the white teeth and the wonderfully hearty laughter, was almost like meeting a traveling theatrical group. We met in the Blue Room of the City Hall on a Saturday; the evening of the dress-rehearsal for the Red Knot opening to celebrate the Fortieth Anniversary of the Scout Movement in Sweden. Boy Scouts and their leaders in great numbers trooped up and down the broad staircase, carrying stage sets to their designated places, dragging signs and curtains, yelling, articulating, while the yellow, blue, red, and white lights played over the vast, empty hall, lingered a moment on the finished scenery here and there, paled and went out like dying fireworks.

I felt a chill across my back.

75

We were only three watching from the dreary emptiness of the orchestra seats—the lady, myself, and our little daughter Lena, who was still too young to see the show but had been promised to see the dress-rehearsal. By and by all the noise and activity on the scene became too tiring, her little head started nodding, and soon it was resting in the lap of the superintendent—now she is just any friendly lady without the official distance, when she takes Lena's head in her tender hands. She is just a warm woman then, and the political struggles are far from her.

Our friendship began that evening and it was to last through many years and many storms; a friendship which also encompassed Boel.

⚜

And what would I have done during those difficult years without Marianne?

Marianne was a delicate German girl who a few months earlier had crossed the Iron Curtain with little more in her knapsack than a student certificate from East Germany of dubious value. She had had no experience in scrubbing floors, baking, or washing children's dirty feet. Her hands were white and small, and she used to say they were lazy.

I learned that her hands were not lazy.

She would take Boel with her when she did the shopping—she was much braver than I. She pulled and pulled at Boel's ego—this alien something that wanted to hide in corners. She never grew tired. Years later—when no one any longer tried to hide the truth behind all wrong-diagnoses—Marianne still was trying to get a response when every new attempt had failed. One memory remains clear in my mind. We had paid a call at an institution out in the country. Marianne took Boel out into the surrounding wilderness and tried to play "Robber and Princess."

Marianne hid behind trees in some new hope that Boel would chase her. Marianne was quick and small, and she didn't mind laughing as if. I still get a lump in my throat when I recall the endless times Boel and I returned home after having driven children to and from preschool for the hard of hearing; there would be cheerful Marianne in blue cotton dress, setting the table, ready for a stimulating argument about life's meaning, or perhaps only a jolly, restful chat; while Boel sat quietly and hummed to herself or rocked.

There was a peace over those days, which I can miss until it aches.

In my childhood the greatest sin was to be stupid.

In spite of the fact that my father was an invalid he completely lacked understanding of the tribulations of a dull mind. A mental defect was incomprehensible to him. Perhaps Providence, in mocking irony, presented him with a grandchild who failed to develop mentally. For by now it had become increasingly apparent to us that the next doctor to see must be a psychiatrist.

"Developmentally inhibited" was an expression that was first being used that autumn by a new society to help mentally retarded children. A new concept was introduced, meant to clarify a condition earlier referred to as various types of backwardness or retardation. The concept encompassed the whole scale of "slow learners," the debile or morons, imbeciles, idiots. This scale has still practical use, even though the labels are avoided, as if thereby trying to ignore the defects they describe. Instead, the difference between the various categories is expressed in numbers.

The number, in turn, is a measured value of the inexplicable phenomenon we usually call intelligence. It is an intelligence quotient—and this has the same magic quality as the verbal diagnosis. It has its own strength, goes its own way. When it exists—if it exists—and is put down on paper, something worthwhile has been accomplished.

The intelligence quotient is an objectivization of something that, admittedly, in its practical forms of expression is too well known, yet gropes in a vacuum as long as it lacks a name. When a quotient exists on paper it gives the impression that something might be undertaken. It is like a peace proposal which—when put into words on paper—creates hope for negotiations.

Negotiation usually means—at least while it takes place—that there is no war, that an armistice exists. In practice war sometimes comes, in spite of negotiation, in spite of words on paper discussing peace proposals. The alternative is peace after the armistice.

Parallels exist. Many. Both the low quotient and the war-and-peace proposal when moved from the strict objectivity on paper to the practical field—in the nursery or in the battle-field of war—become subjective, common, and dull. Seldom do they assume the tragedy one attempts to describe in books. Reality's monotonous gray is their color. Bravery, courage, endurance are words we love to spread over this gray. By so doing we pretend that we have been able to hide the ugly de-tails of the daily routine, all that which from an esthetic or hygienic point of view would be repugnant, perhaps even loathsome.

But—reality we cannot escape in the long run, with our words and our quotients. Death might be beautiful, and it is always final. Mental retardation is seldom beautiful, and it is never final in the same way as death is. Therefore, it is sometimes well not to know all in the beginning, not to suspect the falsity of the words, the uncertain mathematical reliance on the quotient. In the same way as it is well not to suspect that the written peace proposal might exist—only on paper; the day war breaks out it is well not to have suspected it. For war too has no beauty to offer.

In my childhood a "low intelligence quotient" assuredly would have had a better sound than the simple, direct ex-pression which to my father was the greatest sin—to be stupid, wooden-headed. In his later years, when he sometimes com-plained that Providence had robbed him of both health and wealth, I quietly used to remind him of his four children, healthy in mind and body. This he could not understand; to him it was obvious that all his children should be normal.

I remember his irritation when my nearest-in-age brother and favorite playmate—now a physicist working with cosmic radiation—wasn't as good a speller as the teacher wished. Such sins must indeed be punished. I can still hear his piercing yells from the bathroom when a D– in spelling was being thrashed out of the recalcitrant. I can still feel that evening's pain in my stomach, still feel my knotted heart and disgust as I saw his striped behind before he managed to hide his shame under his night shirt. I had great difficulty in getting over this insult to my comrade of the toboggan slide in the Lidingö-woods. In fact, I have never entirely gotten over it.

It was hardly to be expected that my father and his generation should understand. It was not the thing to do to speak of such things in his day. When I cautiously tried, years later, to make my parents acquainted with something of this, my father interrupted me by telling about a servant couple his father had had on his estate in Sörmland.

"That farm couple, they had 'one of those'; who sat in a corner and banged his head against the wall; they never let callers see him. They put food in front of him in a bowl, the way one feeds a dog. And I guess they cleaned up around him when they had to. But they didn't let anyone see him. People knew he was there, they talked about it. . . ."

"Boel is 'one of those,'" I would say. I might even say it with special emphasis, with an unconscious desire to shock him.

"Nonsense, girl!" said my father. "Anyone can see that Boel isn't like that! She's such a sweet and nice little one—come here, little lass and let Grandpa hug you! Look out, Boel! Don't jump on my feet! Don't you know Grandpa has rheumatism?"

"Boel doesn't know *anything*, Father. She doesn't at all realize that your legs ache. She is exactly 'one of those.' Even though she is so sweet!"

"You don't know what you're talking about, Kajsa! That boy I was speaking of, he didn't look like Boel at all. His mouth gaped open all the time, his head was enormous, like a dwarf's. He looked horrible, they said. I never did see him."

"But Father, you don't know how he looked inside the

head—nor how Boel looks inside her head. I don't believe the difference is as great as you think."

My arguments were of little value. This was alien ground to my father—always would be. And now, afterward, I'm glad he didn't have to live to see all we had to go through.

My mother understood better. She clung for a long time to the deafness, but she would also talk of an operation; or perhaps she might outgrow it; or all the other theories that came from all directions in those days. In spite of it all she finally gained a clear understanding. Her imagination was more vivid, her tolerance broader.

The child in the glass ball was no sinner to my mother. She was only a little stranger among us. To be accepted.

The psychiatrist was a friendly, warm, and very busy woman with a long appointment list. She had her office in a special clinic at the university. Her waiting room had an aquarium with fish of many colors, and just as I tried to attract Boel's attention to the graceful creatures behind the glass, a skinny boy with an egg-like head, hairless like a billiard ball, came rushing into the room, turned over the table with toys, jumped up on my knee, threw his arms around my neck and held on so hard I could hardly breathe.

I tried to loosen his grip a little; then his features hardened. I stroked his cheek with mine, touched his forehead with my lips and said slowly:

"You are a nice fellow—what is your name?"

The boy's mouth traveled eagerly across my face.

"You . . . you . . ." he said, "you smell good, you smell candy. I want to be with you. You smell good."

A moment later a worried nurse came and tidied up after the hurricane. She looked in surprise at the boy on my knee:

"Is he really sitting quietly there! Amazing! He seldom is quiet for a second. Usually he doesn't like strangers."

The boy held on to me. He rubbed his nose against my cheek while mumbling almost rhythmically "smell-good-candy-smell-good-candy-smell-good. . . ."

I did not realize it then, but in that moment was born a wish in me, a wish to change course and try new roads; to leave my work in the building-research field, where many—much better qualified than I—could plow further in the narrow furrows that were mine. I did not know that at that moment was ignited in me a desire to devote my mind and energy to an ever-mocking riddle—the human psyche and its limitations.

I held Boel by one hand and a red, rather big, broad book in the other. On the front cover was a picture of a wide tree spreading its many branches, and at its foot grew white flowers; white, pigeon-like birds flew in and out of its lush greenery or rested near its fruit. On the back cover lay a baby on a bed of flowers, white butterflies fluttering above. Across the flowering tree of this front page a banner fluttered with the inscription: *Myself*. It was Boel's baby book.

The book prepared me for questions to be asked, many by now familiar to me. We already had two such books in our family, one for Sten and one for Lena, the brother and sister of Boel; notations about their first reactions, their characteristics and peculiarities. They had become the children's favorite books; there were snapshots, locks of hair, baby teeth, weight records, foot impressions, and baptismal pictures—all those things we people love to gather about ourselves and return to and look at over the years, sometimes in amusement, sometimes deeply moved.

Boel's *Myself*-book had many empty spaces in important places. But it also contained information that might be confusing:

I came into this world on the First Sunday in Advent, November 28, and it has been said that Mother kept back the labor pains to make sure I became a Sunday-child;

I cried like a sea gull;

I *reacted very early to sound and light*. I listened to the ticking of a clock when only sixteen days old, and followed a pointed finger with my eyes when four and half weeks old.

I was said to have a friendly disposition, and the prediction was that I would be good-natured. I made the family happy

81

with a smile on January 2, when barely five weeks old, when my mother came to attend to me. Papa insisted that of course I would have difficulty in keeping from laughing at such a ridiculous sight. For a while I was rather sparing with my smiles, but the rattle Father gave me on January 23 made me happy. I began to hum while hitting the rattle which swung and jingled so nicely. I discovered my fingers on March 1; April 3 I pulled myself up into a sitting position, holding on to Mother's index fingers. I got my first tooth April 22, not yet five months old—and earlier than Sten and Lena.

So far all of the reactions were earlier than with most children, but a turning point, or decline if you wish, could be discerned after her first illness at the age of about six months. I had never been conscious of this until I visited the psychiatrist and answered all the questions with the aid of the red book.

The psychiatrist seemed confused; her almost shyly considerate questions groped for a foothold I could not give. She was undoubtedly more used to solving knots in tightly infantile psyches than in something so evasive in psychiatric experience as a consciouslessly, complex-free soul that hovered beyond any contact in its own vacuum.

She suggested I put Boel in her clinic, so she could observe her for a few weeks. I was grateful—this clinic was small and light and operated smoothly. Outside, the birches were turning yellow in a friendly, sloping meadow; the psychiatrist was of the type who willingly would have exchanged the sterile white uniforms of herself and her assistants for some flower-patterned housecoats. Parents had access to the clinic whenever they wished. I myself practically lived in this hospital some three or four weeks, got to know the nurses, the psychiatrist, and the other doctors, as well as the knolls and stones in the meadow, the climbing stands in the play-yard, and the hidden corners for moments of restful privacy out in the birch grove.

What, then, does one expect from an examination of this kind?

Subconsciously one expects a cure; one hopes one day to

bring home another child than the one put in; in the same way as one would take a child to the hospital for an operation and bring it home all sewn up, minus the appendix.

All those questions needed to be answered, they must have some effect, they couldn't lie there impotently in some hospital dossier for all time? So many details to explain, surely, they must have their place in the pattern. Why would I otherwise have been sitting there answering questions, digging for the reasons?

An Austrian doctor happened to be attached to the clinic at that time. He took the case history. I tried as hard as I could to satisfy his questioning, tried to find parallels. My father? Without straining the imagination one could call my father neurotic, perhaps, in any case a most unrestrained person, with edgy nerves. In his youth he had been struck with rheumatoid arthritis, a happening which undoubtedly had affected his nervous system. That he had lost his good humor with his possessions was perhaps under these circumstances not surprising. But—his mind, his intellect? No—I could help the Austrian no further. There was nothing wrong with my father's intellect. Far from it. And my mother? No, she came from an industrious teacher-family in Bergslagen; all her brothers and sisters had taken care of themselves; two were teachers, one a prominent M.D., the others successful businessmen. A little excitable at times, perhaps, but. . . .

Anyone else? My own brothers and sisters, my husband's family? Other relatives? The older children? My youngest brother one might call a little eccentric, perhaps, in his interest in music, in his early ability to play classical music without notes; another brother of mine had had some difficulty in spelling as a child, but now he was writing his Ph.D. thesis in nuclear physics; my oldest brother was a professor of education at an American university.

On my husband's side the result was equally inconclusive. A number of honest, upright relatives passed in review— Grandfather, a trusted judge, Grandmother's father, another judge, Grandmother's brother, also a judge. No bite here. Not the slightest hint of neurosis. All relatives on my husband's side were able people with fine records.

The Austrian doctor wanted to meet our other children, and I went home to get Sten and Lena. Sten's comment—"Nutty Uncle," and Lena's—"Uncle with kind eyes"—did not add to the picture. And when, at our last interview, I rose to say good-bye to this friendly and thoughtful foreigner my eyes happened to scan his papers. They were emptier than I had reason to believe after these numerous questions, and the main question struck me:

Heredity—0.

Autumn had grown a little chillier by the time I got Boel from the clinic. My last talk with the psychiatrist had been about the increasing possibilities for aid to children with defective hearing, the shortcomings of psycho-galvanic examinations, the psychiatrist's co-operation with the specialist of child-audiology at the hospital, the need to raise money for various retarded groups as had been done through the forty-year-jubilee-gift to the deaf.

When we came to talk of Boel there was less to say.

Many tests had been made—all negative. Of those which had been carried through, physical functions were perfectly normal, something we knew without tests. The electro-encephalogram showed a normal "profile," even though possibly a bit "underdeveloped." From the observations only one thing was clear: everyone connected with the clinic had reacted to Boel's crying; it had affected them greatly.

"I'm worried about her crying," said the psychiatrist. "It is so heartrending. So lonesome in some way. It's impossible to comfort her."

"But Boel hardly ever cries!" I said in surprise. "It must be a mistake." The psychiatrist, in spite of all, even in Boel's case, was apparently unconsciously searching for her own specialty—the emotionally crippled.

"She doesn't cry very often. But when she does we have been unable to do anything about it. One cannot reach her."

At length we tried to sum up our conversation. Boel's behavior was autistic, self-centered. She had the typical looks and behavior of children who had suffered from encephalitis. This group was relatively small. To the best of my ability I tried to familiarize myself with these terms, as if they had been some sort of medicine with possible promise of a cure. There was a suspicion that Boel had had a virus infection in the brain—not meningitis but inflammation of the brain itself. Such a thing might happen unsuspected, like a thief in the night; it was possible that her sickness when six months old might have been the cause. The younger the child the greater the susceptibility of damage to the central nervous system. And the apparent normalcy in Boel—her well-developed body, her sweet face—more than anything indicated some such etiological factor.

Could I have hurt her through overstimulation? Had I attempted to train her too much, or . . . ?

This the psychiatrist did not believe. She said one ought, of course, to be careful with "different" children, but one must yet try to make them leave their alone-world. Assuredly, these children were more sensitive than other mentally retarded, they might react catastrophically to too urgent contact-attempts. But one mustn't leave them to sink entirely into themselves.

"A little child like this one shouldn't be in too noisy or large a milieu—I mean among a big group of children who yell and fight. She should be in a small department where it is quiet, yet, supplies adequate stimulation. A small home, then. . . ."

She stopped suddenly; I thought I could notice her blush. She had entered a field we had not at all touched—Boel's future. She had happened to slide in on the most sensitive question we have to solve, we in this situation. She herself seemed startled that she had stumbled into this track.

". . . for I suppose you haven't, after all, intended to keep Boel at home—in the long run? I mean—a family with healthy children. . . ."

She was considerate, this psychiatrist; she broached the problems cautiously; she developed tactfully the prospects for the future—all of which I myself had pushed in the background—as *if*. She emphasized that one shouldn't rush into these decisions, they must come in their own ripe time. On the other hand, one shouldn't be blind to realistic necessities. What would happen to a child like Boel if both parents suddenly died in an accident?

"Have you ever thought of that?"

I sat dumbfounded for a moment, then I stammered:

"I don't really know . . . no, I guess we haven't thought anything. We haven't thought. . . ."

I walked slowly out of the clinic with Boel's hand in mine. The swinging door slammed shut behind me—I forgot to hook on the safety chain at the top of the door in this clinic—the safety chain against the enterprising, restless little bundles in this department, with their milieu-damages and adjustment problems, who otherwise would run through the whole hospital, up and down escalators and elevators.

Yes, I forgot the safety chain. And now the door closed behind me. This time it sounded more like a yawn than a sigh.

I held Boel's hand in mine. But—we carried no intelligence quotient home with us.

Throughout Boel's short life, there had been many periods of nomadism. We knew of this and did not leave her out of sight except for the shortest moments.

Eventually, the shortest moment was too much.

I was beginning to have constant anxiety for what might meet me on returning home. Each day, or every second day, I was met with hair-raising reports: Boel has run away! Don't put up the car! Drive and look for her! And so we spread in different directions, I driving the car, with irrational turns and stops, sometimes with success, sometimes without result. The Lidingö police by now were familiar with a little girl walking briskly in some direction while humming a little melody to herself. The neighbors too.

One day Sten found his little sister on the railroad right-of-way at the edge of the deep sea; one day Lena found her high on a cliff overlooking the tracks; a third time Marianne caught up with her halfway across the Lidingö bridge; a fourth time in the middle of the highway with cars rushing by in both directions. A fifth time a workman fished her up from a ditch just being built by the water department.

One might wonder how she got so far. The explanation was that we often started our search in the wrong direction, and with each minute she gained on us.

For Boel was a fleet-footed nomad.

When we built our house we listened to our esthetic architect who favored houses without fences. Fences were old-fashioned barriers tainted with social snobbery; modern living called for open gardens, views, perhaps a row of low shrubbery in front.

We never had time to enjoy our open view, and we were forced to raise an old-fashioned, unfriendly fence. This wall gave us some peace, but even the strongest fence has its weak spots, especially when it runs across uneven ground. And there are escape holes under the gates.

Boel soon found the weak spots.

However, there was some consolation—the holes narrowed down the directions of escape. But peace came only with evening, after Boel's door had been locked.

The real peace—for an hour, perhaps.

Then a new anxiety arose on another plane.

What is fatigue? Why do we need sleep? The day's toil is in our limbs; it is also in our heads. I doubt if anyone has tried to measure who is the most tired, who needs sleep the most. We know from experience that the need of sleep varies with different persons, but we know little of the why or wherefore.

Boel's lack of fatigue—was it the result of her lack of mental activity? Physically she was more active than most, constantly at a run from one corner to another and back again like a swinging pendulum. Perhaps she rested at times, but she never rested as other people rest nor did she spend as much time in bed as others.

In bed she would roll and sway, until one bed bottom after another crashed to the floor. She must have slept at times— but when? There was always some sound from her room. I might awaken in the middle of the night to hear the jubilation from Boel's room as she carried on, as she laughed. She was playing as one never could make her play in daytime!

There were periods when her play consisted of tearing long pieces from the wallpaper. I turned off her light. Darkness had no effect on her—the wallpaper was torn from the wall and lay in wads on the floor next morning as usual. There was nothing wrong with her night-sight, then; I only knew that one day there would be no more wallpaper fairy-tales to tear down, no more blue-colored stories from Hans Christian Andersen.

But wallpaper lasts longer than one would suspect. And nights too. With the years they became many and long. For six years my own need for sleep was reduced in relation to the possibility of obtaining it. I never slept more than two hours at a stretch; my entire sleep, under favorable circumstances, did not exceed four hours.

I comforted myself with the thought of Napoleon who was said to have managed with four hours' sleep.

What is there now, afterwards, in the light of memory, that seems most striking in the fate that was Boel's and ours? Many years later to see the children of friends who were born at the same time? Today, as I write this, those children are in high school; they can count, write, talk, read English, and are beginning to attend teen-age dances. It still startles me when those children greet me, as if I were startled that those children could greet anyone at all.

What else? The problems of hygiene, sounds, mannerisms, as I have tried to describe them? One gets accustomed to those things. One finds a solution, one way or another. In our case the sounds and the nocturnal exercises affected the sleep of the other children to an extent that it became necessary to put Boel in the most distant room in the house—the guest room on the first floor. From there the sounds penetrated only my sleep—not purely acoustically, I believe, rather telepathically. I felt that Boel was awake and that something was going on in her room, and that I must get down and see about it. And when I strained my ear I could hear.

She might have soiled her bed—this happened about every third night, one never knew exactly when; then she hummed in disgust—I had to fill the tub down there, lift her into it, and undertake a general cleaning up under great outcries of protest, which might awaken the whole family upstairs. Sometimes it might happen that one of them appeared in the bathroom door to inquire why in all the world we made so much noise? In the middle of the night?

She might laugh loudly with building blocks and strips of paper flying about her. She might grunt angrily and bang her head against the wall. I never knew the cause of the sounds, and I had to get down and find out. This, also, became a habit, part of me.

What was it, then, that could be called striking?

Was it her habits in eating, so peculiar, so unreasonable? First she used to like porridge, gruel, buttered bread. The gruel—with the beautiful baby on the package—was for a long time her favorite food; she might devour three plates at a time. Then one morning the romance of the gruel was over. When the plate arrived at the table, Boel was seized with fury; her hands grabbed the plate and turned it over, the contents spilling over the table and onto the floor. For the next year she refused the gruel; indeed, she refused any liquid food from that day on. Now the food must be solid, preferably firm and fried. Meatballs and fried potatoes now became her favorite dish. At last I gave in, against my better judgment. I gave her meatballs and potatoes for the sake of peace.

Eventually I tried to have my meals alone with her.

What more? What more can I tell?

The isolation. Not only the one Boel herself had built up. Not only the walls, the invisible ones, around the child in the glass ball. No, all the other isolation. Never a children's party. Never any little callers. Never a playmate.

89

Yes, I did arrange Christmas-tree-parties for Boel, as for the other children; there was a present in her stocking, but Boel herself was not there. The present had no meaning for her, Christmas meant nothing to her.

The shops? I avoided them. In my car sat a child who swayed and rocked in her aloneness, waiting perhaps. It was a question of locking her in the car, or being exposed to endless interrogation in the shop. I gave up shopping.

Anything else? I do not remember. Boel was the child in the glass ball. Christmas, birthdays were celebrated as usual. But—Boel was outside. In that land beyond she played away her days. Her care, the purely practical, was not beyond my ability. The pressure lay not on that plane.

It lay in the search, so futile, after something ever elusive. It lay in the emptiness, the infinite emptiness, of search to reach the child.

A little child who never had come to us.

I remember still the dreams I used to have now and then, perhaps every second month. While she still was so little that she was in her playpen, I had the first dream.

The dream was quite clear; I can still feel the secure, hopeful warmth I experienced at first, then confusion and doubt— was it really only a dream? Finally a certain almost listless disgust—well, it was only a dream. This time too.

Boel was standing in her playpen or outside in a meadow, the sun streaming through her rye-blond hair. Or she was running—straight toward me. No escape, no avoidance. Her look was with me, right in mine. She might stop in front of me, or come right up to me. To me—not to some goal behind me, some hidden, invisible goal which I never will know.

She is with me. Her eyes are with me, her look nowhere else. The moment is infinite and short, but vivid as nothing else. Now her voice comes to me. She says only one word, but she says it clearly:

Mamma.

Her voice I shall never hear.

VI

Again a new spring had come—one of the many I wasn't able to catch up with. The trees had burst into leaves without my noticing it, and one day our knotty birch against the hill was covered with verdure; it seemed only the previous day it had been bare. The crocuses were already drooping.

The springs had always been like that for us. Filled with work during the sunny hours they stole away, and when the rush was over and time more relaxed the full summer was upon us in all its brilliant recklessness. And every new spring we thought—next spring, then. . . .

A new spring had made its appearance, and with it a new expectation. For a time Boel would be in the background.

I had cautiously started to orient myself toward a new field of activity. Together with the assistant professor of audiology at the big training hospital I had written a pamphlet on auditory training and educational advice for deaf and hard of hearing children. This had required both practical and theoretical studies, and now I had the taste of blood; I wanted to go on in this new field.

But now a new expectation had been born and pushed everything aside. This infinitely golden *Expectation*. The sun literally shot its ray over our mustard-yellow house; in its generous wastefulness of these last spring days it blew itself up to an enormous, gleaming balloon, a glittering, boastful promise that might explode any moment. Everything swelled and grew.

And I was expecting.

This expectation had in previous cases filled me with a calm, peaceful joy, as bright and calm as some bay in the Eastern Sea on a summer evening. It had been so then. It was so now.

The misty gray, the daily commonplace, all the thousand and one painful moments faded into as much indifference as the shrieking headlines in the morning paper concerning power politics. Everything changed dimensions. All plans were made over. Everything happened only for the moment, from day to day. The future need not be taken into account.

Because the future was within me.

How to explain this that happens to a woman when a new life has been created within her? At first she has the situation well in hand. It is she who carries the seed. It is she who controls the future. And the future grows within her, makes her broad and heavy, presses her feet against the earth. Each day inexorably closer to the earth. There is a secret, a dizzily sensuous joy in this—to be pressed against the earth ceaselessly. Inexorably.

But one day, when all is over, perhaps even many years later, she discovers in horror another change: the future is no longer within her. It isn't even with her. The future has passed her by. When the future left her womb it assumed its own life in a way she had never dreamed.

Now she stands on the side; she already belongs to the past, and sometimes she shudders at the discovery. She might think of how it had been, search among her dim childhood memories: was it so here, at that time too? When did Father and Mother become the past? When did their participation in reality come to an end? Her throat might tighten a little—in anguish, nostalgia, and relief, all in one.

Mother and Father became old when I began to think. Then they became the past. And I owned instead the future they had had. When I was ten they were already ancient, re-living the memories of their youth, greedily sucking at their fleeing sweetness. They must have been at the same age I was now, or would be in a few years. Yet they were old, and life no longer was theirs.

So it would be for me also. Perhaps this made me so happy at every new expectation—that each time it brought with it a new delay. In practice one blames it on one's love for children; one could imagine as many as possible. Yet, perhaps this is only part of the truth. One loves not only children, one loves oneself also. One wants to have one's part of the future, play one's part on the stage. Once more have one's role in life. Life itself.

This time, however, it was something particularly especial. I had had to wait longer than usual; I had begun to despair, begun to wait with impatience. In greatest secrecy I had gone to a doctor—not to one of those who participated in my search for Boel's soul.

The doctor laughed, said it was the silliest thing he had ever heard. Thousands and thousands of women walked the streets of Stockholm, scared to death that they might become pregnant—and here I was, a married woman, already mother of three, complaining! At first he laughed, then he grew angry. He said I ought to be grateful that I already had three. Didn't I know the town was full of women who had become neurotic because they had no children, or because of undesired pregnancy? I ought to be ashamed! Come to him and talk of worry!

I could not feel ashamed. Nor could I tell this doctor what had happened to one of my children. I said, with a calm that seemed to puzzle him a little, that no objective reason for worry ever does exist. I knew quite well that many might consider me enviable, but only I myself could decide this problem of my desire, my wish for a new life.

"My worry is mine," I said. "Worry exists in all degrees and is as great or small as one feels it, be it the torture in a concentration camp, or the annoyance at a spoiled permanent. The degree is not for you to decide. It is hardly your specialty. A piece of music is beautiful only when someone listens to it, a play exists only when it is performed, a picture has color and life only when an eye sees it. So also with worry. It exists only for the one who feels it, and it is exactly as great as . . . ."

The doctor interrupted me by saying that the consultation would be twenty-five *kronor*, that his waiting room was full, and that, according to the headlines, a new liquidation was taking place in Czechoslovakia. I blushed as I fished out my bills. There was no need for further details. The doctor had his pattern to follow. That was all.

But two months later my expectation was a fact. And I enjoyed it in the way that was my own, only my own.

The summer grew hot and heavy, and the family took off for the mountains. Boel stayed close to me; she had her plastic bath on the lawn, and as she ran around naked in our garden she could splash to her heart's content. My waiting went on peacefully, this time free from apprehension. The hot July sun became a warm August with dark evenings.

During this summer a new problem had presented itself at my door, a problem along the lines of my new field of work. There was a doctor at the university-clinic, about my own age, who was busy studying a method to measure hearing in young children. He had to write a paper—as these doctors constantly do—and he had a great many numbers and different methods for audio-metric test-results to assemble. But he did not write easily, and he wrote unwillingly. During those days, we started to work together, a co-operation that opened new perspectives. It also started a friendship between both of our families that still exists. He was to specialize in the audiology sector of child-otology.

Boel was not using her hearing in a way that gave sense. I recalled how I one spring evening, while listening to a blackbird, had begun to speculate over the emotional value of sound. I thought I had learned to understand the essential, the all-important, i.e., the difference between sound as such and sound as we perceive it. Now I would have an opportunity to further study this, get a clear idea of the limit of each function-measurement, where no co-operation existed.

This was too stimulating to allow me the rest so essential in the ninth month. And I would soon pay for my eagerness. Fortunately, a keen and capable gynecologist—with big ears, a kind smile, and glittering eyes—discovered my sin through a too high percentage of albumin. I was greatly thankful to him when he put me in the hospital and looked after me, better, I believe, than I had ever been before.

And when the time was accomplished, a girl was born.

Riken came into being—without the aid of gas—in that wonderful happening which is a birth. And during the happy days that followed, Boel's shadow paled somewhat.

The nursing time became a sort of pause to get my breath. Almost without noticing it, I left one research field for another. I approached the fragile construction which is the human psyche and its functions, and left step by step the more stable concrete foundations and their aspects in building-research. One day I must know more, but as yet I hadn't decided how.

As I said, it is hard now afterwards to describe that period; it was a sort of interregnum. Bengt had one of his busiest periods. Since all his periods are busy he must during this time have worked at a killing pace. I myself was happy. My wound was beginning to heal. Sometimes, when out driving with Bengt at my side, I felt this new happiness potent about us, and I would say silently to myself: This you must remember! Thou shalt never forget! This is our time! Remember, just now we are enjoying our time! Perhaps it will not last. But it is now.

"Go around! said Bøjgen." Hadn't I thought of this diabolic admonition in *Peer Gynt* that time when I fought with my conscience for the sake of the Inconvenient One? There is a limit to the ability to function, I had said to myself; a limit one cannot force. One cannot always "walk right through." One must choose. Sometimes one chooses the roundabout way. So obvious and natural. And that road sometimes looks like the only possible road. Perhaps otherwise one couldn't even have gone on.

We don't realize that we quite often push aside the obvious when we deal with a handicapped person, someone who disturbs our sensitivity. We try to be tactful. Of course. And our surprise might be great if we were told: "Go around, said Bøjgen!"

My father, hadn't he been the first one? In painful shame I can remember times, when I stole by, when I closed my eyes—in order to go on myself. Close the eyes, pretend, give excuses, go on, draw a line, don't push too deep, don't get your fingers burned, what you don't get mixed up in you don't need to get out of. The practical person has words, a thousand and one, appropriate and with an incontrovertible sound, for this one, this same: "Go around, said Bøjgen."

This the practical person has, because he must have his peace to act—he thinks. He must have his reason left intact—he thinks. And sometimes we take the road of the practical person.

❧

Those golden-rimmed days that were ours during the first year of Riken's life were like an armistice which we shall always remember with nostalgia. Boel was in our periphery.

However, one small episode got me to thinking and somewhat disturbed my peace of mind. I was ready for my nursing hour with Riken when I heard a yell from her room. Most of the time she was happy and good, and the cry told me she was in pain somehow. When I reached the room Boel was

96

standing at the bedside of her sister. She had scratched Riken in the face. I thought of comforting the baby when it suddenly stood clear for me: it was not Riken who needed comfort.

Something inexplicable had happened, something I hadn't counted on: Boel had made a visit to our world; she had tasted the fruit of jealousy. When I hugged her in my arms and said: "Mother loves you just as much, my little girl!" one of her rare smiles lit up her face.

It was a short visit, a brief look-in on our world. She had shyly opened the door ajar, on all of us, before she turned her face away from me.

When I lay down on the bed to give Riken the breast, Boel was lying beside us, humming.

I rested in the now and enjoyed my rest. Because I pushed Boel's problems into the future did not mean I considered them solved or insoluble. In reality, they were there all the time, rather unchanged, now and then taken out and examined in the light of some new actuality, the way it is with us who face this fate—that our fulfillment remains unfulfilled.

Unfulfilled? Yes, the way we look at unfulfillment in the Welfare State, identifying it with the not entirely functional. Not statistically acceptable, in other words. Measured with that measure our fruit, our fulfillment, is unfulfilled. This cannot be denied, nor would anyone seriously deny it. But—is the measure, the *scale*, always the right one? Who is in the long run the more productive, the more "socially useful"?

As I sit at my desk a long row of names passes in review, soon to be forgotten—Jorgen, Anders, Magnus, Torgny, little Kristina, Gunilla, Liselott, Elisabeth, and many, many, and again many others. Names I might mention, of hands—feeble and anonymous—that do each his or her part, perhaps not strikingly, in a work that yet grows with unknown strength. A strength with multiplication effect.

I remember once, out in the country, I was looking out through a bathroom window. Below was a rubbish pile, pieces of concrete from a wall, bits of bricks, sooty plaster. Right through the middle of the pile grew a straight flower, the most regal of all flowers; in the midst of the rubbish a sun-flower grew.

I like to remember that sunflower when we work together, we with this fate, every time something is accomplished, accomplished by our children's anonymous hands.

"You mustn't wish someone happiness! That's a horrible degradation!" I was to remember this statement some of us made one of those days when we were still in college. By and by I was to remember that remark—remember it and ponder it.

That spring we rented a summer-place in Sörmland, an old cotter's farm near a lake full of fish. It was not a very large place, yet roomy enough to house all of us, in a beautiful setting. We had outgrown Klövsjö, regretfully. Boel could no longer share a room, and this had become a new problem.

The two-story farmhouse had been built for two families; as we wouldn't need the upstairs kitchen it could be used for a washroom, or at night as an emergency bathroom for Boel. An ideal place for the child in the glass ball. It was a house our large family needed.

But there was no fence.

A new nomad life began. The shore was long, with an outboard motor at the pier, and steep cliffs above the reeds. Opportunities for escape were numerous. Boel had grown; her legs were strong and fast from much training.

That summer I sought my peace in two ways; I would pack all the family in the boat and set out for a little island in the middle of the beautiful lake where we were relieved of worries. Or, I would let our little nomad run on an upstairs balcony with protective, solid walls. There, in the space of a large-sized room, she would rush back and forth, back and forth, the warm sun beating down on her.

And the time was approaching when we no longer could push aside our problem; soon all of us must face it.

But while summer still lasted I kept my eyes closed to it.

In the long run, however, a seeing person cannot keep his eyes closed. With the arrival of fall Riken began to walk. This became a sort of reason-to-attack to Boel. Two, three steps and —bang! The push need not be very hard, but it had its effect. And finally Boel laughed—at the right time.

Children will learn to walk, though, for the human race is hardy. Children will learn to walk at the proper time. They will learn to speak at the appropriate time. Riken had a natural ability to conquer hearts, so my worries never grew to any proportions. Moreover, this autumn I made a decision that was to give me extra work, indeed, much extra work, and I tried to bury my own worries in this effort.

My husband and I shared our love for the deaf and our hate for deafness. I was longing to do something more worthwhile than transport children back and forth. We agreed that I should devote some practical effort to the Boy Scout Movement; I who was neither a Scout nor a specialist in deafness.

I was sworn in by my husband one evening, up in the forest glen among the pines and knolls, under heavy night dew and torches of peace. A light was kindled for each paragraph of the Scout Law I swore to uphold. A group of our friends had gathered for this simple ritual on the shores of Lake Mälaren.

That autumn a course was given at the Institute for Deaf in Stockholm to instruct teachers in preschool auditory training; during the course they attended classes for deaf children as observers, and the following midsummer an "examination" would take place. We were a dozen of us, I guess, but I was the only one to attend classes at the university simultaneously, a somewhat hectic program that would eventually lead to a master's degree, of the "quickie" sort. For I was in a hurry; I felt I could devote two years, at the most, on an education that had only one purpose in mind: to learn more.

Two years. During those years the seminar at the Institute for the Deaf was to result in a reward beyond expectation. The professor in charge of the course was perhaps in some respects the only one in his field. He was also the director of the Institute. It still gives me a jolt to have to write of him in the past—he burned himself out very fast; our friendship had a run of eight short years.

The first time we met had the usual, unavoidable dull and gray color that our human intercourse demands. He was an official of remarkable zeal, in behavior so unlike the friends Bengt and I met in the upper eschelon of the Scout Movement where a total absence of conventionality held sway. We met, then, under utmost formality. And yet, when I was to write his obituary after his sudden demise many years later, it was this very first meeting I was to remember:

"When we first walked through the long corridors we met a little girl; she was in the first year of the eight-year curriculum during which time it is the lot of deaf children to be separated from their families. The girl stopped us and jumped up at her director. He no longer had eyes for us—the formal callers at his big institution—he forgot us entirely, picked the girl up in his arms and stroked her hair the way a father might. The long corridors and halls had been touched by a magic wand, turned into a home."

This man, with seriously friendly, soft eyes, a funny walk, his head a little askew, became a remarkably stimulating teacher during this unforgettable course. He spoke long and well, as does he who moves in the world of the silent, but our talks never seemed to have been futile as is often the case in conversations. They were important. No one could, as he, open vistas into that field of communication—human speech.

Fate, so inclined to incidentals, has willed that his widow, after long and loyal service in her husband's efforts, today is the very important helper I long sought in our work among those so far beyond conventional understanding.

But again I'm getting ahead of myself. The course at the Institute for the Deaf had begun in August; behind me were three years of daily intercourse with deaf children, a great deal of theoretical study in the field, a special course in leadership for handicapped Boy Scouts, and many contacts with deaf adolescents through observation in classes for the deaf. I considered the time ripe to dare a participation in the Cub activity at the Institute.

I will never forget my feeling of gratefulness to one of the experienced den-mothers when I asked her if she would help me with a Cub pack for the little silent ones at the Institute: Yes! she answered without hesitation. She became my alter ego, my Akela; we complemented each other in this work, she with her better understanding of Cub activity, I in understanding the deaf. A co-operation that was to stretch over many years, to bring values I would not wish to have missed. At first we were almost touchingly naïve in our work. We had to try so many times before we appreciated the limits. And many disappointments were in store for us.

We would sit in a ring on the floor of the dreary attic room —fourteen boys and we two. The frosted glass in the ceiling let in an eerie gray light; the janitor watched us apprehensively at the door; I could hear my heart beat. I had written a simplified "first lesson," an introduction to the jungle world which is a normal Cub's natural flight of imagination, easy to light, but sometimes just as easily extinguished.

I began my part, trying mimicry to the best of my ability, using every imaginable variation of changing modulations, although hardly expecting them to get through. Neither my friend nor I had any idea how important is modulation for the understanding of speech even among us "normal" ones. We knew very little of the stunted imagination in deaf people, and the paucity of stimulation with the absence of sound. We expected response—to enthusiastic commands, to suspenseful curiosity. There was no reaction. Why? When we had made so great an effort?

It was the director at the Institute, above all, who gave me the explanation: Cut all the links in the long chain of association which an idea, a word, has to us—cut them all on either side of the middle link, which is the word itself, the idea itself in concrete nakedness, and you get the deaf child's conception. For the rest of us the links flow together, so imperceptibly, so closely forged together, that we no longer notice, nor are able to analyze how the chain once was formed, from the first acoustical stimulation, never perhaps to reach the threshold of consciousness, to the last link, so enriched through endless processes of purification; this one, again, never remaining the last, only the latest among ever improved links. Each link depends on another. To a deaf child there is only one link. Can a link and a chain ever become identical?

Later, while studying Gestalt psychology and its theories at the university, I was constantly struck by the fact that so little research had been done in the field of imagination among deaf people. The Gestalt psychology was mentioned in our course, as one field among many, a speculative curiosity, a by-product of philosophy, something no serious psychologist would bother with any longer. Perhaps this is so. But our first Cub instruction in the Institute attic became more than a practical illustration of the importance of the theories of Gestalt psychology.

It became a complete failure.

The child-otologist whom I helped with his thesis on hearing-measurement or audiometry for preschool children was nearing the completion of his studies this winter. My own studies in psychology had to be forced—I had been given an assignment to rewrite a book on handicapped children written originally in English; my course at the Institute for the Deaf flooded me with a multitude of books to be read—naturally to be expected by the conscientious director; my Cub work with the deaf little boys must have a new approach; Riken was at the always-grabbing stage; and again I was carrying a new life within me. No wonder that Boel—the child in the glass ball—during this time played her solitary games at the edge of my consciousness.

Since, I have often thought of this. Had I already made my decision? Were there, after all, no alternatives to choose between? I no longer know. I only know that I was washed along on a wave of activity, too strong to be stopped. The nights were the same—filled with all the sounds from Boel, her uncontrollable outbursts of happiness or anger. They suited my working scheme. No longer any nocturnal wakes with unproductivity; I arranged a special study in a closet on the first floor; the proximity to Boel's room made me feel I had a right to be there. This little cell had its advantages: it had no windows. When I used it during the daytime I did not know if there was snow or shine outside; our big birch on the hillside did not tempt me to look out. Decidedly an advantage.

And during this spring term a new chore was added: I met Leif.

Leif was a spindly sort of boy, at the wide-eyed, curious age of six. The remarkable doctor who had been a dentist had one day asked me to take charge of Leif's auditory training. My course at the Institute was not yet completed, but Leif could not wait for a certificate, or a degree in psychology. It was his time just now. He had only a few months available for training at the ancient school for the handicapped, and these months had to be used.

We became friends. Every morning as I entered the long hall a Jack-in-the-box figure on a special tricycle came rushing toward me. Our instruction began at the moment of greeting. Leif suffered with cerebral palsy and loss of hearing from the injured brain. But he had a usable residual hearing. His paralysis was of the type called athetoid, and—as usually is the case with people suffering with this—he was happy, lively, an extrovert. He taught me many important things; my own problems assumed other proportions during the months I worked with Leif at the old school. Until a new happening would put a dramatic end to our activity.

We collected pictures, Leif and I; we cut them from papers, we pasted them on cards, practiced their names. I did the cutting, I thought he was too slow. And I wanted fine pictures with even edges. Leif's fingers did not obey any definite impulses, they slid hither and yon. The more anxious he became, the more lively grew his hands and fingers. With such hands one could not cut good figures from a paper.

And that was how I became the one to cut and to paste, the one to button his coat or shirt when I wanted to take him out in the car to enlarge his range of vision. Constantly I was ready to aid, help get going, put in order.

Today I know how wrong was my action. I did not understand it then, but today I know.

Often the best help one can give the handicapped is no help at all. This paradox had possibly touched my consciousness already in my childhood—my father had provided that illustration. But I had forgotten.

It is so easy to put limits about the handicapped. We say that such and such he can learn, but this never. We don't test whether or not he has reached his limit, nor do the schools. We do not test the elasticity of the limit, never change the goal, once the limit is fixed.

There was much Leif had to teach me that winter.

Perhaps the new life within me in its way aided a re-examination of Boel's future, helped ripen our decision to investigate the possibilities of placing her in some home or institution. Now afterwards it is very difficult to point out exactly when our thoughts turned in that direction. I only know that there was once a time when I couldn't imagine a separation from our child, when my thoughts always ran along these lines: either both of us go, or neither. Anything rather than this.

By now I know that no road is the right one to all. There is no rule as to the time for a decision. Each one must ripen according to his own rhythm, make his own decision, the one that seems best to him. Many of society's zealots—those who sit around the long conference tables and make their decisions—have such irrevocable opinions that one is struck dumb in humble admiration at such omniscience. There are many types; from those who declare that society ought to remove from the parents all right of decision in this important question, to those who say the parents should remove from society any right of decision in this important question.

104

Well, truly astonishing. And yet . . . .

Whatever the final decision, it is always the wrong one, it will never bring the expected peace to the restless. The peace one longed for will mockingly take its leave, alter its shape or dress.

I had known it in advance. I knew already that the short and happy time—our time—soon would be over. I knew that in the future there would be with me a permanent guest whom I never could get rid of. This guest would be sitting at our table at mealtime, be at my side in my daily chores, step up to my bed in the evening, and remain at my side during the night. Indeed, my life with this guest would be very intimate.

My conscience, ever sensitive, ever watching, would be my guest and companion.

Yet I felt our lot was better than many others'; fate had granted us more opportunities to choose; I myself had chosen a field which offered contact and understanding. Both our united efforts had during the past years opened so many unexpected doors that in whatever direction we turned we would meet a helping hand. Yes, I was more fortunate than most, and I knew it. But—my guest knew it too.

And again the day would come to add a little to my pattern, although I didn't suspect it at the moment, nor discern the connection in the beginning. An unknown lady brought me this bit of my pattern.

The two of us were sitting, one on either side of an enormous desk, in the general headquarters of the Scouts. She had the solid, respected authority of a big newspaper behind her beautiful features and delightful elegance, and I—I had an eight months life within me, and a febrile work lust to overcome. Our contact had been made through the State Superintendent of Special Education, the lady with the wonderful laughter.

"And then we have the feeble-minded, or the mentally retarded as I think you call them now," said the lady. She

105

was the hard-headed journalist, but in spite of her formal reserve she was not able to hide her engaging warmth and tender heart that shone through. "Have you any suggestions? How do I go about getting contact with some of them? How get hold of a mother who has had the experience?"

We had been talking about deaf children, and I had just advised her to look up my friend the "Värmland Pine." The journalist lady was planning a series of articles about "those different children"; I thought I had discerned in her voice that this was a personal concern to her, beyond the limits and ambitions of daily journalism.

No listener has a keener ear or a clearer eye than one who is personally involved, more involved than journalistic duty calls for. I felt this, and it gladdened me. We needed her assistance, hers and many others'. I was anxious to give all the help I could. The Värmland Pine had just, over the telephone, granted an interview without hesitation.

Now I picked up the receiver and called the lady psychiatrist. With a voice full of expectant confidence I asked for a name of a woman with a retarded child.

I had not thought too much about this request or what it really meant. It seemed simple and without complications. Only a name, suitable for this purpose, perhaps a case etiologically interesting, even dramatic. Something for a casual circle of readers. That was all. I had asked for nothing more.

Slowly, thoughtfully, I replaced the receiver. I turned to the journalist lady with some effort, looked at her in silence.

"Well, of course, . . ." I said at last. "Of course she is right. I hadn't thought of it before. She cannot give out any names of *those*. It hadn't occurred to me."

There was no irony in my voice, none. Only a tired statement; a statement of fact. I still don't believe that it ever had been in my consciousness before that anyone would hesitate.

It had never occurred to me that there was any reason for secrecy, anything to keep hidden. When I called the psychiatrist I was anxious to help, in the same way as my friend the Värmland Pine. Now, at once, I realized the difference, the infinite difference: this concerned something more than just the deaf—another class.

I had never thought of this, this class distinction between mentally retarded and other handicapped people. Since, I have often met this concept, become intimate with it, even felt a certain wild exuberance; as if I had taken part in some political fights of old, having the occasion to climb the barricades and fight for my class, its equality, its fraternity.

At the moment I was only mildly puzzled, a little embarrassed over my unlimited naïveté and lack of good advice. I sat there, across from the journalist, feeling poor and mentally twisting my helpless hands.

But the journalist lady was not helpless.

The first article she wrote—in a series of many for her fine paper—was one of the most beautiful ever composed about those "who have not the full light of their minds." And it was to have consequences of utmost importance to me personally. It was written on the theme "A World without a Key," and in the title role was Boel Maria Elisabet Junker.

VII

Urgency fired me. Life seemed filled with demands clamoring for attention. But time was greedy. I don't believe I seriously wanted it to be otherwise; I wanted to live fast, if this were permitted me. Yet—the urgency smarted intensely, the demands piled up, I couldn't see over them however much I tried. Taller and taller they towered as my time drew near. And sometimes I was in a dilemma, pressed between time and demand.

Consciously I now pushed aside the thought of Boel's immediate future; I harbored some irrational hope that something would come on the stage to make all decisions superfluous. Perhaps this is true with many of us, we wish subconsciously that Fate—something from outside, not to be swayed by our will or action—will interfere. At one stroke it will solve everything. When our need for it is most pressing it will lift the heavy burden of responsibility from our shoulders.

But fate did not interfere, not a fate to assume my responsibility, cut my knots, and indicate the easy road. No, an entirely different fate was in store for me. And while all of us gradually arrived at the conclusion that Boel must be taken care of outside the family, and while we discussed plans for how to best arrange this, the fate stole closer and closer. This time no premonition warned me, as had been the case with Boel's arrival. No inexorable portents darkened the light April days. Only the restless urgency.

I had just managed my first step on the academic ladder during this sign of urgency; my book about handicapped children had gone to the printer. Leif with his cerebral palsy lightened my tired mornings; he would rush to the long corridor, hide among the potted plants, perhaps to get away from the usual morning smell of soap and lye, anxiously awaiting my little black Citroën.

About eight years earlier my then boss at the Governmental Building Research Institute, a man with a stimulating, healthy appetite for research, had planted a seed in my mind which since had grown with many weeds about it; now it had to be attended to. At the time my inquisitiveness had tackled the most difficult of all: the function of language and its effect on—and from—our visual perception. In other words, our perception of visual stimulus. Had language any effect at all that could be measured? How was the world seen by the dumb? How speechless is he, after all, this person who does not have speech spontaneously? How much of what we see assumes color and shape from the words we have, the language we use? What is speech and what is language?

All these questions had piled up. Now they called for time to be investigated, answered. But time, so short and never returning, became greedier for each day. And at last there came the day when no more respite could be given: time had run out.

Yes, the day came. No one had looked for it just then, or in that way. It came anyway; uninvited, unexpected, without considering that it was not wanted.

I had aroused enough energy to telephone my professor in psychology for an interview. I wanted to discuss with him my curiosity concerning deaf children's visual perception, and at last he promised me time. I felt an elation that is difficult to explain at the prospect of airing this subject with high authority, listening to my professor's point of view.

I rushed from the telephone upstairs, wild to get back to my study-cell below, to prepare myself for the interview of tomorrow. I remember I thought to myself: amazing, that I can move so easily with barely fourteen days left!

This I had time to think, and enjoy a certain pride in it. Then it happened.

It was a moment's work, as the expression goes. A moment is short, it might be long enough to draw a breath, pant, wink. It can also encompass a crucial part of a life, a fateful future.

My moment brought Fate with it. I did not at first realize that this was so, it did not at once disclose its true identity. I only had time to realize that I had slipped on the stairs, that I slid down a few—I don't remember anymore how many. My amazement was great when I collected myself sufficiently to see what had happened.

My right foot seemed to stand out at a right angle from the leg.

. . . but this the doctor must take care of . . . O Lord, I haven't got the time . . . how will I manage this . . . get to the professor tomorrow . . . lucky I hadn't let the maid go . . . how to reach the telephone, the extension downstairs . . . these steps have always been too steep . . . how often haven't we fallen on them . . . how could any architect plan such a steep staircase . . . and that window up there, one can never get to it to wash it . . . wonder if I can get the foot back in joint myself . . . how funny it looks . . . how many miles to the phone . . . why is nobody at home . . . never when needed . . . how will I manage to get to a doctor . . . I must call the professor and tell him I can't come . . . strange how the foot stands out like that, can it be so . . . telephone . . . telephone . . . take it easy . . . but I must call and see if I can get hold of a doctor . . . perhaps I can drag myself to a car . . . everything'll be all right in the car . . . only get to the phone . . . easy, easy now. . . .

I held my hands around my right leg; thus sitting I tried to move my body, step by step, downstairs. Near the bottom of the steps I interrupted my peculiar way of locomotion, stretched out my arm through the railings toward the telephone, pushed my body against the posts—still another ten inches. I made another effort, pushed still harder against the railing. Yet, still ten inches to the telephone table.

I must try to get around the last post, get down on the floor . . . then, then the pain began, intense, stupefying for the first ten minutes—one or a hundred, which? It was so intense that I almost lost consciousness.

But I must reach the receiver in some way, I couldn't get help by giving up. Someone was bound to come home soon, all would be well. The maid couldn't stay out the whole afternoon with Boel and Riken. Sten must be home from school—Lena couldn't play forever.

That a foot with this appearance should hurt seemed nothing to get surprised at. And pain, after all, is pain, and can be endured when one knows its origin.

At least I thought so.

Suddenly I espied the telephone cord, dangling like a snake over the back of the chair. Had it been hanging there all along? Hardly a yard from where I sat. How had I missed it?

At once I became quite calm. I grabbed the cord and began to pull the telephone towards me. It worked. When within reach I dialed, not nervously—my hand was calm—the number of the taxi station. While talking I remembered I had no money, I had spent my last cash in the morning. Well, I couldn't drive myself with such a foot, they would have to take my word. Then I called another number, to my capable uncle, who had been my childhood doctor and taken care of my infected throat, my throbbing ears; I remembered his number and needn't look for it in the book. His practice had recently been taken over by our good friend who had written the thesis about audiometry—he devoted a few afternoons each week to private patients.

111

As it happened this child-otologist was in his office.

"Could you get a doctor for me, I believe I've broken my ankle. Quite badly."

"Are you crazy?"

"I don't believe so. I believe I've broken my leg or my ankle and must get to the hospital. I just called a taxi. . . ."

"Taxi! You must take the ambulance! I'll call the hospital for an ambulance. This is very serious—is there someone to help you?"

"No one is at home just now, but I expect Sten any moment. I'm sure he can help me."

"But you must have someone to help you at once! And be sure to take the ambulance!"

"The taxi is already here. The trouble is I have no money, I spent my last penny this morning, didn't think I would need it like this."

"For heaven's sake, don't worry about money! I'll give you all you need—I'll rush down to the hospital at once."

Now I became apprehensive. Was it really so serious?

"Well, I'll take the taxi," I said. "You try to get me a doctor to set my foot."

"Of course—I'll meet you there."

I was sitting on the steps, waiting. Outside was the taxi, ticking away money all the time, and suddenly the house was full of voices. The maid came back, Sten returned from school; Lena helped telephone my husband's office, but Bengt was not in.

"I don't think you have broken your ankle," said Sten. "It would hurt."

"What makes you think it doesn't hurt?"

"You don't cry."

"Well, I'm afraid it is broken," I said. "And I'm going to the hospital right now. Won't you help me to the car?"

Sten wasn't quite fourteen. Now he looked at my leg and thought it was horrible. He hated hospitals, but did not hesitate for one moment to accompany me, come what may.

The doctor on duty turned out to be a young man I didn't

know. I hoped he would admit me, even though I hadn't arrived in an ambulance.

❧

I guess it must be so—there are rules to be followed; but just when I more than ever needed a warm helping hand it was as though a door had been slammed in my face. Is this really necessary? Here I had arrived, an unknown case, in a housecoat that had swept the dust off the stairs, in torn stockings, accompanied by a thirteen-year-old—not in ambulance! I needed the hand more than ever; why had it disappeared? I didn't get it.

I wonder how those many others are received, those who don't raise their voices and demand attention.

Someone reacted at last. Someone seemed to have heard the boy explaining that Mother couldn't walk, she had broken a leg, she was expecting a baby. A stretcher was finally rolled out. I crept up on it with Sten's aid, conscious of a new inner strength I hadn't suspected I had: I had a life within me, and I must have attention! I had set my mind on raising my voice and calling for attention.

"What shall I take down? Shall I write you're pregnant?" It was the young intern on duty sitting at a desk, scratching his head irresolutely while watching me on my stretcher. "And then you have a leg injury, haven't you? Does it hurt?"

"Hand me the card! I'll fill it out myself!" I said with rising fury. "I've been on this stretcher long enough! No one here seems conscious of my predicament—a broken leg and advanced pregnancy! What am I supposed to do—yell and carry on to get attention?"

"Take it easy—I'll manage the card," said the intern sleepily and hurt. "Only—I don't know what to write."

"Don't you see I've broken my leg?"

"Well, I'm not sure of that from the looks of it. I think I'll write 'pregnancy'—or 'advanced pregnancy', perhaps?"

"Good Lord! I'm in the ninth month! I expect my child at Walpurgis-night, barely two weeks. I suppose it is 'advanced'!"

113

"Well, I'll write, then, 'extremely advanced pregnancy'—
that should do it, don't you think?"

"Do you expect me to lie here and dictate to you? If you
don't have any competent doctor in this joint to examine me
I might as well get back home!"

At last the doctor on duty appeared. He looked briskly
impersonal. He pulled a little at the foot, nodded, then patted
me lightly on the stomach. I was conscious of infernal pain
in my leg.

"This girl isn't expecting her baby today or I could set the
bone immediately."

Girl! I was expecting my fifth child and he called me "girl."

"My dear boy," I said. "You had better stop pulling my
foot or something is going to happen." How had we got into
this supercilious talk? Did we expect the foot would right
itself from such nonsense?

"Does it hurt much?"

"Do you think my foot would look like that for the fun of
it?"

Now he seemed startled; he bent down to look closer:
"We'll have X rays taken right away. And then we'll get a
gynecologist to come and look you over."

At long last the first word to indicate a certain interest in
the new life within me. At last there was a new atmosphere
in the room, an atmosphere that hadn't been there before.
I turned my head away. No sense to brood. No sense to try
to find out if the pain was endurable or not. An accident
department. A department for cases, not individuals. More
than elsewhere this was the department for cases of this large
hospital where a spirit of friendliness often had greeted me
in other connections, and I marveled at the efficiency of this
great institution, handling so many cases, yet so few with a
fatal outcome. But where does the surgeon get his lack of
fatigue, his light indifference? Must it be so?

Suddenly I knew. Of course it must be so. How would he
otherwise have the strength to go on with his knife? If the
surgeon were involved in the individual behind the wound
he would never have time for the decisive, lifesaving opera-

114

tion. And at once I see my stretcher in another light. Even the receiving-nurse must have her coat of mail, with no time for nonsense. Perhaps it is even a useful device—this to meet roughness at first: a certain guarantee that no one comes needlessly. The weeding out has been done already at the front door.

So my thoughts wandered while I was being pushed through long corridors. The young doctor had at last realized that my foot hurt. He even considered my case so urgent that he told me to call immediately if I noticed any decrease in the feeling of my toes. He instructed me to urge the X ray personnel to rush me through.

I had been left on my stretcher in the X ray department. It was after daytime rush. I felt lost in this desolate forest of technical apparatuses. Someone had left me, and I had had no opportunity to call out that the feeling was leaving my toes, that it was urgent. Outside the door I heard steps departing, someone calling far away:

"Anything else?"

Someone else answered, hollowly: "I believe a foot came in. Some accident. . . ."

The voices trailed away. The hospital seemed deserted, empty. I could still hear the echo of the departing steps, then they died out—and time stood still. A man's voice, far away. And the woman I heard a little while ago. A little while ago—half an hour ago!

"There is a foot in there—that's all we have for now. . . ."

I didn't want to lie alone any longer, I didn't want to be an anonymous foot that could wait. Now I threw all caution to the winds. It is against my nature, but the fear made me strong, swept away any scruples I might have had to use means of this kind. I called at the top of my voice: "Nurse! Come here at once!"

She appeared at the door.

"Nurse," I said. "Will you please call the head doctor to come here at once. We are old friends, and I wish to talk to him now. At once!"

This was something I had wanted to avoid, but I dared not wait any longer. The head doctor of this department was a student friend of my husband, in years past we had spent many happy evenings together. I was now sufficiently frightened by my evil-looking foot to employ a method which I sincerely detest. But blinded by fear one will rush to where one hopes to find help.

Presently the room around me was no longer empty. The nurse regretted that the head doctor had just left, only five minutes ago. He must have been there when I arrived, I thought. However, the young doctor in charge was already very busy about me, two more nurses appeared from nowhere. The sensation in my foot was still there, but my toes felt cold, and this I didn't like. Weights kept my leg in position; the infernal pains were not alleviated through this. Now my foot was X rayed from every possible angle quickly, efficiently. Now everyone was busy with me. My astonishment was great.

Suddenly the room was empty again. I closed my eyes, tried to lock my imagination out. I was again alone for a moment, the room empty. I tried not to think, not to worry, yet a vague apprehension seemed to fill me. When suddenly a new voice reached me from behind my head:

"Well, well! How goes it? This time Dr. Junker is asking you."

Thank God, I was no longer alone. It was the voice of my husband. A sense of security came over me, and I didn't worry about how my toes felt. Everything would be well, nothing would happen to me now. His hand held mine, warm, good, strong. He would take charge, as always when it was only the two of us.

This new security exhilarated me. A broken leg—how trivial. I had someone with me to decide, and surely all would be well again.

It hardly hurt any more.

"Why did you twist your foot like that?"

"Thought it would look better that way," I laughed, and now there was a lump in my throat, in spite of laughter and exhilaration. "Don't you like it?"

116

"Aren't they going to do something about it? It must hurt . . ."

He walked toward the door.

Now there was activity everywhere. I was handed stacks of X rays to carry with me and my unborn baby and my broken leg to surgery. No delays now. Now security was at my side and nothing was overlooked. And fear had departed.

My friend, the child-otologist, too arrived; people were all around me. Much talk over the X rays, my husband and the otologist had consultations; I waited, now without worry. I had been wheeled into a private room. Again the door opened suddenly, and the young doctor in charge appeared, another doctor at his side.

"This is a very complicated break—we must operate immediately." He was definite now, no supercilious talk. "And you might have your baby tonight, Mrs. Junker."

"Tonight?" I said in surprise. "But it isn't time yet. It isn't due until Walpurgis-night. And I've no labor pains, only pain in my foot. . . ."

The young doctor raised his shoulders lightly: "The anesthesia," he said; nothing more.

At this I was on my guard. I was fully awake now, no superciliousness, fear, or pain interfered. I was alert to consequences immediately; I had read tomes of medical books on the subject. My voice was clear as I said:

"The anesthesia? Do you think the anesthesia would have any effect on the child?"

Again he shrugged his shoulders.

"Does anesthesia usually affect it?" I persisted, and I remembered all I had read about gas injuries, interference in oxygen supply to the fetus, about cerebral hemorrhage in connection with operations on the mother, and similar cases. "Is it absolutely necessary to operate?"

The doctor looked at me in astonishment: "My dear Mrs. Junker, you have a compound fracture. It would be futile to do anything but operate. I thought you understood that?"

"And . . . and it is your opinion, Doctor, that the anesthesia might in some way affect the baby?"

117

"Not necessarily, Mrs. Junker. I only said, you mustn't be surprised if the baby were born tonight."

"But I don't understand," I persisted.

"The anesthesia," said the doctor, laconically. He held a syringe in his hand.

"You mean, the anesthesia in some way brings on a delivery, is that it, Doctor? Or what have you in mind?"

But I received an answer no longer. The doctor seemed to have disappeared, and everyone suddenly was in a great hurry. I was aware of my husband at my side for a moment, our friend the otologist also. He asked if I wanted anything, if he could do anything for me. I was thirsty, I wanted water. But water was just what I could not have, nor anything to eat. The first injection had already started to take effect—my lips felt like paper; the otologist wet a piece of cotton and held it over my mouth.

"You mustn't drink water you see. I am sorry. Soon you will be operated on. It'll be over in no time—we're only waiting for the chief surgeon."

Now I was confused again, perhaps because of the morphine. Wasn't the doctor-on-duty going to operate then? No, they had called the chief surgeon himself, they had had trouble in locating him, he had gone to some party, but the otologist assured me he was already on his way. They were getting everything ready for his arrival.

"But . . . but why the chief surgeon?"

"You must realize, Karin," said the otologist with finality, "this is a very difficult compound fracture. And your condition makes the case so much more serious. In cases of this kind they always call the chief surgeon in this hospital. They don't just go ahead and operate on a woman in her ninth month. I've looked at the X rays myself—it's very ugly. But don't worry, the chief surgeon is a specialist in this field, the best in the whole country."

"But . . . but . . . how can a fracture be so serious? People break legs every day, and no one thinks much about it."

"Remember, my dear, you're going to have this leg for the rest of your life . . ."

118

"But the child . . . what'll happen to . . . ."

"Don't you worry now."

✖

I never had time for worry, or for reflection.

Too much happens at an operation to allow the patient fear or apprehension. In a semi-comatose condition one is removed to an unreal theater with a dim impression of distant actors—the doctors, the nurses, the technicians.

Spinal anesthesia. It sounds professional but here it becomes frayed like the figures around the operating table. Much easier to say "a spinal." What a strange feeling this—the "lady without a lower body." I remember something like it in my childhood; at least my brothers always had a booth for such a phenomenon in our play circus in the yard; I remember one summer out on the island I had to represent such a lady—a lady without a lower body.

Now I was again playing this same role. I no longer knew what was happening to the lower part of my body. A group of white-coats were busy there, at my head stood a serious-looking figure with an oxygen apparatus, nurses ran back and forth in their gauze masks, their eyes ever alert. Sounds of rubber gloves against instruments, then—suddenly someone had appeared and all was ready for attack.

"Let her rip! Junker!" said the chief surgeon as a greeting.

It was an unusual greeting, from an unusual man. He was an enthusiastic sailor, would even sail in December if he could get out through the ice. The greeting referred to a book my husband and a friend of his in the Scout Movement had written together some years earlier. This relieved the tension, and at once I forgot my leg. With implicit confidence I surrendered my lower part to the white-coats down there at the foot.

"So you're a sailor too, Doctor!" I said. "What kind of boat do you sail?"

Between his short, quick instructions to the young interns around my leg the doctor would from time to time regale me

119

with sailing incidents, quote from Bengt's book with flattering appreciation. I was beginning to wonder if all the activity around me actually was real—it didn't seem to concern me or the child within me.

Presently I felt short of breath, I fought for a moment a choking sensation. The intern at my head was quick with his oxygen tank, his guard-duty was efficient and immediate.

Then I was conscious that something was taking place that had nothing to do with my leg. In spite of my lack of feeling I was aware of beginning labor. I had a peculiar "outside-of-myself-consciousness" that a motion within me was taking place, a motion that I could neither aid nor control. A sort of painless motion. I was only aware that the doctors at my feet exchanged glances above their white masks, perhaps someone got a needle, but it was all unclear to me.

The atmosphere had changed; there was no longer any talk about sailing, all was now urgency and tension. And I kept snapping for air, eagerly inhaling whatever I could from the oxygen apparatus. All the others were intensely busy, no one was short of breath except me. The young anesthetist's eyes were acutely observant; he followed my breathing as if it were a case of drowning, I thought.

Ghostlike—surely this is a good description of the strange atmosphere during an operation; the funereal white from the spot lights, the white shrouds enveloping doctors and nurses.

I had been instructed to inhale more oxygen at the slightest feeling of nausea, and I obeyed willingly. Now it was very silent, the "marionettes" were performing their exact roles, according to directions not familiar to me.

Then a thought came to me—and no one controlled or influenced my thinking—it simply appeared: now I am about to have another child with a handicap.

Was my thought audible? The anesthetist bent over and asked:

"How do you feel?"

"It won't be well with the child," was all I said.

He threw a glance toward the anesthetized part of my body, but didn't say anything. He had nothing to say.

A nurse hovered at my bedside the whole night through. It couldn't have been a quarter of an hour between each time she peeked through the door. Did I really go to sleep? I do not remember. All I can recall is that the whole night was filled with the same question from the nurse:

"How do you feel? Any labor yet?"

I remember she felt my forehead from time to time, my pulse occasionally. And each time she lifted the blanket and felt my still insensitive abdomen.

"How do you feel? Any labor yet?"

Already quite early in the morning I was moved to another department; my bed was wheeled into the delivery section. The capable and friendly gynecologist who had attended me at Riken's birth—he of the kind eyes and the big ears—was now at my side, listening, examining. The sensation in my lower body was gradually returning, and with it progressively increasing pain. And the pain was labor pain, this I knew.

"I still don't believe anything will happen as yet," said the gynecologist with concern. "Are you sure they're real labor pains?"

"My dear Doctor—this is my fifth child. By this time I know what labor pains are."

"Well, I'm not so sure it'll come yet. . . .'

"But it must! It can't be good for the child if it doesn't come when it hurts so much."

"How often do the pains come?"

"About every third minute."

The pains did come often. Through the whole day and evening. They increased according to expectations. I could not imagine they would end except in one way—exactly as before; with the arrival of a noisy little life.

For more than twenty hours the pains kept on. When they gradually abated I wondered if I ever had had them.

&

"I'm worried about the child. I'm sure the operation couldn't have been any good for it. And I wonder why it didn't come when the pains kept pushing it for so long."

It was Akela who had come to visit me in the hospital. She had brought drawings made by the deaf Cubs, and she was telling me about their questions. They had asked her, through signs, if I had—bang! We both laughed heartily at her imitating their priceless gestures, how difficult it had been for her to make them understand I had broken a leg instead of giving birth to a child. The lack of connection between the two is, of course, quite un-understandable.

"But now that you are over it you needn't worry about the child," she said. "Don't you feel better?"

"No, that's just it; I have small pains every evening, without results, and it isn't natural. And I have a feeling that going through an experience like an operation, and a whole day's real labor pains afterwards, must have damaging effect on the little life."

"Let's hope you're wrong! You've said right along that your child would come at Walpurgis. Let's wait and hope for the best!"

"One can always hope—but I don't think I'm wrong about the child. I want to believe—but I cannot."

❧

The days passed. By and by my foot no longer hurt more than that I dared hop about on the healthy leg, dragging the cast along. I was, indeed, well enough to go home so as not to take up a bed in the surgical ward. Everyone seemed to have forgotten about the child—except me.

On the floor everyone had learned about the unusual case of the woman who hadn't had her baby, as all had expected. One day an assistant head nurse stood at my bedside. Her voice was shy, as if burdened by a guilt similar to mine.

"How was it now—didn't I hear you have a little child, Mrs. Junker, who is . . . ?"

"Developmentally inhibited," I filled in, "or retarded, if you will. They used to call them feeble, but that doesn't quite cover it. There is certainly nothing *feeble* about our Boel. If anything I think she is too active. Why do you ask?"

122

"I was only wondering . . . do you keep her at home, Mrs. Junker?"

"Yes, she is at home."

The nurse's eyes were now moist. She lowered her voice, a twitch around her beautiful mouth:

"I too have a daughter who is . . . like that . . . I . . . please, forgive me, Mrs. Junker . . . but I can't keep her with me. She is in a home now . . . but I don't know . . . don't know. . . ."

She blew her nose, looked around guiltily, and whispered: "This is inexcusable for a nurse, to act like this . . . with a patient . . . please forgive me, Mrs. Junker."

I took her hand. My own eyes were moist by now.

"My dear, why shouldn't you tell me? We in the same situation must stick together."

"I don't know if I've done the right thing."

"You mean by putting her in a home? How old is she?"

"Eight. We managed till she was about five or six. I have two boys also, and I'm alone with the children."

"Of course you've done the right thing. No one can say what is absolutely right or wrong. Each home is different from every other one, each situation different from every other. Only you yourself can decide what is best. Only you know— no one else. I myself have considered sending Boel to some place but haven't gotten to it yet. Probably I'll have to now."

"Why now?"

"Because I have a feeling I'll have another defective child."

"But my dear Mrs. Junker, there is no reason to say that. Your foot is healing well, all your reactions are getting back to normal."

She studied the curves and the figures on my chart. The blood count was beginning to be normal again, sedimentation was falling, pulse and temperature were moving in expected curves. No exceeding rise to cause secret worry.

"I'm still worrying. I can't help it," I said.

"One is always worrying," she offered, "all of us who are in on this. And one never knows what is right. I'll never get it into my head that I've done the right thing. And yet—there was nothing else to do."

"It's always that way. All of a sudden there is only one thing to do, and yet it's always wrong to do it. It's the same for all of us."

"Thank you so much, Mrs. Junker, for listening to me. It's such a comfort to talk to someone who understands this thing."

"I don't understand it. But I know how one feels, and that's at least something."

❦

The day had arrived.

It was Walpurgis Eve, the students' day, a day we always had celebrated together. In the early days we used to be with Bengt's college friends at Hasselbacken, always ending up with the marchers at Skansen. All those beautiful years in the old times when I never managed to get my dress ready in due time, we had been singing the hymns to spring; dancing at the ball till late morning. How young we had been those days celebrating with youth of all ages the arrival of spring, hope for the future.

Now again it was Walpurgis Eve, a little chilly, perhaps, but a promise of spring. Again the songs were sung on the streets, the fires lit on hilltops in various parts of the city.

The pains had come all day long; Bengt had been sitting at my bedside for a few hours, his comforting, good hand close to me. I tried a smile: "Don't you remember? I said right along this child would come on Walpurgis Eve."

"I remember. But you aren't always exactly punctual."

"This time I aim to be punctual."

The day's festivities had penetrated even our delivery floor, every possible excuse for the evening off had been exercised by nurses and attendants. And I hadn't even had the sense to give birth before eight o'clock when change of personnel took place.

124

Again I was alone in a delivery room, and this time the reflexes on the frosted windows from flaming May-fires seemed to me like fluttering figures of anxiety. Now and again the sound of distant rockets came in through the open window, but only seldom, very seldom, did a pale-faced, overworked nurse appear at the door. No answer to my frantic ringing, and I was beginning to fear that my "Walpurgis-child" would arrive without assistance. The cast on my leg was exceedingly annoying to me, and there was cause for fear.

At last someone came, perhaps at my eighth ringing. She was a tiny nurse, her coat blood-stained. She was not going to festival dances, and she did not seem to have time to stay with me either.

"Is it anything special, Mrs. Junker?" she asked in a harassed tone of voice.

"Only that my child is about to be born. Any moment now. It is my fifth, so I know what I'm talking about. Are you in a hurry?"

"I am alone at the moment. We have eight mothers giving birth—we have only half the help we need—everyone is at the dances. The poor doctor is running from one to another."

Eight women in labor—one for each of my eight ringings.

"Will you call my husband, if you can manage. Ask him to take a taxi and come at once. At least I'll have someone."

New waiting. The minutes either dragged or rushed in *tempo furioso*. The moment was drawing near so fast that I was calculating the normal speed of a taxi, the number of miles per minute. Perhaps there was traffic congestion because of the celebrations, who could tell? Anyway, I was sure my husband was not arriving with a race driver, the time it had already taken him from Lidingö to this hospital.

At last the door opened.

"Thank God, you're here!" I groaned. "The child is coming any moment and there isn't a soul here. They're all out celebrating and the poor devils on duty are working themselves to death. Thank heaven, you're here!"

He sat down on the high, uncomfortable stool at my side, this escort of mine in the spring of our youth.—Do you remember how we used to go out and dance on these evenings? Of course I remember. And I always had trouble with my dress at the last moment. Do I! This is another kind of Walpurgis Eve . . . not the same kind of dance for you and me. Maybe not, but we'll manage. You never were much for dancing, but you always took me out that evening; that was quite sweet of you. I don't know if it was sweet of me, if I hadn't come along you probably would have gone with someone else. And I couldn't take that chance. I remember I was always a little late, but this time I am on time. Well, rather late this time too. Not too late. It's going to be a Walpurgis-child . . . right? Right.

❧

The child was a Walpurgis-child. Through the narcotic fog of the final labor I heard a woman doctor say in surprise: "That was the finest placenta I ever saw—I must show it to the interns."

With great professional satisfaction she was examining the afterbirth which had just left my body. I myself looked at it and admitted it was magnificent. Like a colored illustration in a book of anatomy. But—should a placenta really look so fine, so undamaged?

It hit me like a chill, and suddenly I said: "This cannot be right. Could it be because there has been interference in the food supply to the fetus lately? A human placenta shouldn't look like this—it's like a horse's."

"Nonsense, Mrs. Junker. Why do you think it means anything?"

"Well, I just wondered. It's two weeks since the boy first tried to be born. Could this fine placenta mean that all the advance labor was completed then? Could there be some connection, Doctor? Because in that case. . . ."

"My dear Mrs. Junker—the boy looks perfectly well. I can't see anything wrong with him. He is exceptionally fine-looking! I don't understand what you mean?"

"He has taken a long time to get himself born. Too long a time. That is what I was thinking."

126

"You needen't worry, Mrs. Junker. Now I must show this placenta to the interns."

❧

Already during the first week of Anders' life I was wondering if anything was wrong with him. I watched him every minute while I gave him the breast, and every moment he was in the room with me at the hospital. I talked to the doctors about my observations. All were of the same opinion: few babies could have stood such an inspection without something being discovered.

Brainstorms. Imaginations. I had done too much reading in my furious rush to complete the psychology course. A fine boy. Nothing indicated the operation had affected him. At least not yet. One must be patient and choke stupid thoughts.

We called him our little "coachman," a name in our family for people of reddish hue; also for smoked, specked sausage. We thought this name suited him well. But soon the serpentine streaks across his forehead paled and disappeared.

By the time we left the hospital our little "coachman's face" had conquered the hearts of everyone in our family.

❧

"Now it came again!"

"What came?"

"That faint contraction. I wonder what it is—why does he do that?"

Bengt came in and looked at us. I was lying on the bed giving Anders the breast, awkward as usual with my cast.

"He looks the same to me. It must be something you imagine."

"It happens every time I give him the breast. Awfully strange it seems. Suddenly the whole right side of his face is seized with a contraction. It reminds me of an old person who has had a small cerebral hemorrhage. You know, old people who have aphasia."

127

"You have read too much. You've stared yourself blind with Boel. There isn't the slightest likeness."

"There *shouldn't* be any likeness, that isn't what I mean. There never was anything wrong with Boel's right side. But Anders has it—he is going to have trouble with his speech."

"Why should he have trouble with his speech?"

"Because speech and the function of the right hand are intimately connected."

"You talk as if you knew something about such things. I don't think you know what you're talking about."

"I hope you are right."

Anders was only three weeks old. There was all reason to hope.

❦

"I forgot to tell you—some woman called several times when you were in the hospital and asked for you. She had read the article in the paper about Boel and insisted she had to talk to you. She had an unusual name—I wrote it down here. . . ."

Bengt handed me a piece of paper. At the time neither he nor I knew how important that name would be to us. On my return from the hospital we had again discussed Boel's future. I had been advised that room could be made for her in a new home, a large, modern institution, erected in conjunction with the city and county, and I felt I should be grateful.

I was grateful.

But no gratefulness can replace apprehension—that great it can never be. I knew there was only one solution now: to accept gratefully. And my fears grew.

I wanted to delay as long as possible, bribe fate so to speak. I used every possible excuse for delay. And my fracture aided me in this; I was promised Boel's place would be kept open until I was able to get around better. At least, my foot was now a blessing in disguise.

Meanwhile, I put in a call to the lady with the unusual name.

128

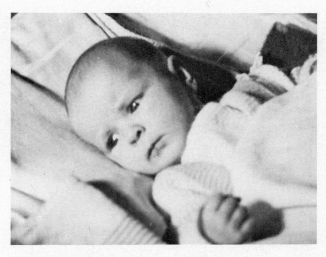

We would call her Boel. Of course she must also have a few extra names—Maria, after her father's mother; Elisabet, after her mother's mother. Boel Maria Elisabet Junker. (Boel, 4 weeks.)

A wall grows up slowly, unnoticed, the defense-wall around the child, round father and mother, round the family.

The sun plays with her blond hair . . . small tunes come from her mouth, I recognize the little melody. It is the same as always, as before. (Boel, 20 months.)

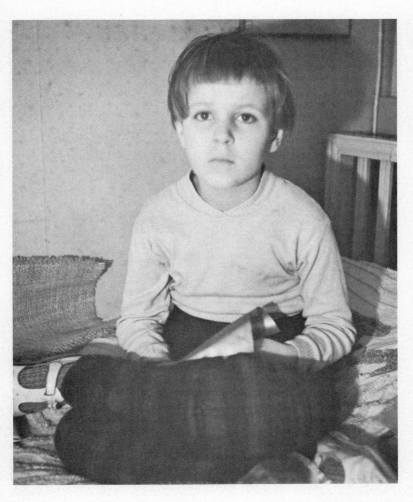

The child in the glass ball . . . around her the aloneness was immense and overwhelming.

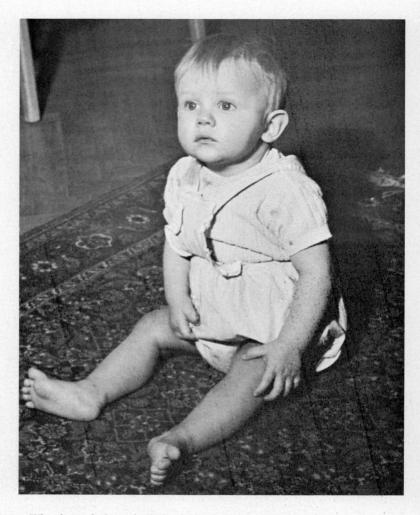

Why do we look at the little child who didn't get to be like all others, who happened to be a break in the beautiful pattern of uniformity, why do we look at it in another way than we look at a flower or an insect that didn't happen to be like its neighbors? (Anders, 10 months.)

Anders keeps busy, he is interested. He is with us, not somewhere else—like the child in the glass ball.

Boel does not suffer, she lives within the frame of her possibilities.
(Boel, 12½ years.)

Anders has taken his first step into the world—he has shown compassion. (Anders, 6 years.)

"By this shall all men know that ye are my disciples, if ye have love one to another." (John 13:35.)

Inger. You are gone now, and I can no longer tell you how much you meant to me. I tried to tell you every time we met, but your shy, reserved smile prevented in me any display of gratitude. I was trying to tell you that it was you I had to thank for my peace of mind. But you wouldn't let me.

We would talk in a new way, we understood each other on a wave-length all our own. We would sit next to each other on our excursions into the country, to see our children. I kept on talking with a sort of patented courage, you would smile with a touch of embarrassment. We were trying to get to know each other, we had met comparatively late in life. At that time we knew little of what lay behind each of us, nothing of what the future had in store. We could only gain our knowledge from the present.

We would talk about where we might travel to learn more. We talked about the famous professor in Copenhagen, the specialist in infantile speech defect. We would take our girls to him. Perhaps. If we could manage. If he would give us an appointment. We would travel to Scotland together. By opportunity. We would look into what the Anthroposophists were doing there; you thought it might be something for our girls.

I listened, and thought: Doesn't she realize that that would be too good to be true? That isn't for us. On the other hand —no harm in looking into it. You were always the hopeful one, I the skeptical. I don't think you ever had time to stop hoping.

And now you are gone. We didn't have a chance to say good-bye. Now it is too late to tell you all I wanted to say. For example, the meeting last summer with the president of the American National Association for Retarded Children, the woman chemist and her husband, this father who said that the good thing with our children is that they have no conception of the future; how I would have liked to tell you this, just you. I myself had not earlier reflected on how fortunate this might be. Perhaps this concept might have eased the anxiety that was particularly yours. And is mine.

To one without hope for the future—isn't it wonderful to lack a concept of the future? We might have speculated on this and perhaps found comfort in it.

The story of you, Inger, and of our short friendship, is the story of the things that never happened. Never. Because there wasn't time. As usual. We thought so much—planned and thought. But were denied the time.

I can't forget the day when Anders was especially in my thoughts—my leg was still in its "luxury-hose" as the sailor-surgeon called my cast—and Bengt was digging in his vest pocket for a note: Here is a piece of paper—I wrote down the number of the lady who asked about you; she had read the article about Boel, and she wants to talk with you. I guess you should call her when you have the time.

That was the beginning. I repeat it once more because it was so important to me. A chain reaction seeks its own way, undirected. A pattern is formed, to all appearance from inconsequential incidents, without apparent relationship to each other. I can only note how a busy journalist's part of the pattern was to join yours, Inger, without her or your suspecting it.

I remember how I looked at your name—spelled wrongly, by the way. And no wonder, you had such an unusual name. I remember I thought, well, perhaps I had better find time to call—she is probably one of those who *know*; who has called because she has so much information on the subject; a thousand and one suggestions; to tell me that Boel's behind must be kept warm, then she'll outgrow it. Or porridge on her stomach, or boiled linseed oil, or massage for her hair roots, or prunes, or carrots; or perhaps she knows someone who knows a doctor who knows; or perhaps she is one of those who wants to get rid of the government; or threatens with the day of doom. . . .

But you were not anyone of those. You were different. Not many days elapsed before I called; I must have felt subconsciously how little time we had. I was dragging along on my

130

crutches, did everything with difficulty. I thought, with some irritation—so much irritated me in those days—better get it over with. And yet, I felt an urgency, in some way. It was something I must do and not delay any longer.

And then I called. We hit it off at once. You said our girls seemed so much alike. I told you I had just decided to place Boel in a home, that new big one down-country. You said you had just been thinking about the same place. Could it be nice there? It is the most modern in the whole country, I replied. But, you said, it is—it is so terribly big. A child will disappear as it were. But the various departments are small, I retorted, without conviction. Yes, you admitted, but not as small as one would wish. And then you told me where you had Liselott.

Come with me and see for yourself, you suggested. I have broken my foot, I said, I can't drive my car. I'll come and get you, you said. I'll only call first and find out if it's convenient. You did call, and it was convenient.

It was a sunny day with bursting birches, the coltsfoot already wilting along the roadside, the pavement glittering and glimmering as it does in May. We kept talking, trying to size up each other, I guess. I remember how I tried to get you down to earth, place your feet on solid ground. You escaped me, wouldn't accept. You wouldn't even hear of limitations, so obvious to me.

Boel was sitting in the back seat, humming. Occasionally she yelled out. But her vague look was unaware of the new fields that passed by. Just her usual, blank look. But a few times—I remember especially as we drove through Södertälje and the picture outside the window suddenly changed character, as it does when one drives through towns—something new seemed to come to life in her veiled eyes. She rocked back and forth on her seat, her faint rhythm mingling with the sound of our Volvo motor.

"That's exactly like Liselott does," you said.

"Does she?" I said. "Perhaps all of them do the same."

You laughed, a little reserved as always, perhaps also a little embarrassed, as often.

"Perhaps so," you nodded.

131

Then the little white house. And the atmosphere down there.

A home, the way a home is. Some shortcomings, something to be desired in painting and dusting. A home. Far from any comparison with a hyper-modern institution, with perfect paint, and no dust. A far cry from tiled walls and sterilized bathrooms, endless formica boards and rust-free kitchenware. Indeed, I am one of the first to realize the importance of hygiene as something useful and necessary. But—there are so many kinds of hygiene, and the most apparent ones are not always the most important to us.

The atmosphere. A light, big living room. An old, beautiful Chippendale sofa, perhaps not the best playpen for children, but homelike. A home with a living room where children can come occasionally. On birthday parties, Sunday afternoons for example. Or other festive occasions when children are there, in the living room, and learn to realize that not everything is a toy to be broken. Exactly as in an average home. They too have living rooms; nine families out of ten in our country have living rooms.

A home. The worn toys are in a heap in an upstairs room —not at all like the toys in an institution where they are placed in orderly rows in the nursery, utterly clean, pedagogically perfect, but without the personality of a teddy bear loved to death, and seemingly little desired. No, there is no use in comparing the two worlds—each one has its own advantages. One might as well compare coins from different countries and pretend they belong to the same system, although with different values. This simply should not be done, it isn't fair, it would come close to forgery.

The tall birch outside the living room window had leafed out more than her cousins along the road, exactly like our ancient birch at Lidingö always was ahead of all other verdure. This birch too was rather knotty, and its hanging branches almost touched the lawn and were already summer green. The lawn itself, here and there broken by fruit trees in haphazard display, was as spotty and unevenly mowed as lawns in real homes where more urgent chores take predominance.

Boel at once walked straight into the home. She sailed right by the inviting dining room table, smiled her own smile, and headed for the old sofa in the living room. Perhaps she recognized it, in the way one recognizes *home* before one even has seen it. She laughed, pushed a child here or there perhaps, and started to run from wall to wall. Her jubilation rose—she jumped, she collided with Liselott—without noticing.

And Liselott didn't notice her any more than she was aware of other children or objects. She was busy winding a long piece of cloth round her fingers, whipped the air with it, hummed, and started to jump up and down. She sang a little tune; it was the leading motif of the Ninth Symphony, just the simple melody everyone recognizes. It can be played on a toy ocarina that has only five tones. But Liselott sang it correctly. Her humming came from another world, a world with no speculations about nuances in feeling. Perhaps they might sing the Ninth Symphony like that on Mars if they sing there. Mars people—at home in a world where our nuances don't count—perhaps sound like that. The thought cannot be brushed aside; it offers a possibility which no one can directly deny.

As we left the home Liselott smiled absentmindedly and without regret.

❧

I always felt big and clumsy next to your delicate frailty, Inger. Like a sturdy marigold next to your fragile, sensitive lily of the valley. We sat side by side at the meeting of the Society for Retarded Children; we visited together at the big institute where I had had to place Boel for a few anguish-filled months, when Bengt was in America.

You trembled like the lily of the valley in a spring gale that time, you could not endure to see as much as I, the marigold. Your scent was fragrant, elusive; mine was more pungent, more enduring. Your stem was more sensitive to knocks and lack of water, it wilted so much sooner; mine was sturdier, more resistant to drought—although I well know that no stem is strong enough to endure all droughts.

The lily of the valley and the marigold—not only are they of different species; their time of blooming is different, at different seasons. Spring and fall. Still I can hear in memory the light, thin tones that belong to the lily of the valley. You played the piano down there at the home, for our girls, always returning to the same melody. It was as if you subconsciously sought to reach back to that melody, it suited you so well. Delicate, brittle, I still hear it: Dance, my doll, while still in youth. . . .

Fate then had brought this about. Your impulse to call me that time, swayed as you must have been by the sensitive observations in the newspaper article about the different child, Boel, was to offer me a key to a home for my child. Neither of us knew it then. Now I know it, gratefully, when I am unable to reach you.

I will always mourn you as one mourns that friendship which never was allowed to bloom in fullness of kindred-relationship and simultaneousness, but which never had time to wilt into mawkishness. Perhaps the friendship in full bloom never really exists, because it must begin to wilt at the moment of blooming. If so, then I'll mourn you as you were to me the short years we sought for this friendship.

I've been talking at length about my friendship for and sharing of interest with Inger because it seems important to me. It did not concern us only, not a private business between me and a woman who left this earth too young. Our knowing each other has a message. It represents a principle, and this principle is important.

She offered me her hand, the proverbial straw, when I most needed it. She obeyed the impulse to seek a contact which she believed could benefit both of us and our children. She did not shy away when a place had been indicated in the pattern, our mutual pattern, the pattern concerning all of us. It is this principle of mutual help I have tried to emphasize in telling her story.

134

I will always remember it when I myself offer my hand toward someone else in our long chain, we who have this fate. In so doing I offer my hand to her in thanks, and my gratitude obligates me. It must be so, that we are all forged into links in a mutual chain. We must follow this principle, all of us. All who can.

She is beyond that heartache that was hers always. My own will remain with me, always, but I find some comfort in the knowledge that Liselott has a home, in spite of all. Both of our girls have a home. And I cling to this knowledge even though fully aware how transitory it might be. Each day granted me is a comfort with this knowledge intact.

I think Liselott is happy. I know Boel is—as far as she can be. I would like to see all the others happy, as far as they can. And I would like to see us all prepared to offer a helping hand when occasion demands.

As Inger reached me a hand.

VIII

5-5. Anders is growing well. He has an expression of awareness and seems jolly when he isn't angry. The children have
already seen him smile, Grandmother also. Unusually early,
but I don't think it is really a smile.

5-27. Anders' smile is now so apparent that no one can
deny it. He had, as usual, a contraction each time I gave him
the breast today, but so faintly I could barely notice it, and
I have not yet been able to point it out to anyone. It's always
gone before anyone gets close enough to see. I don't believe
it will be of any consequence. Perhaps half is in my imagination.

5-30. Begins to lie awake for long periods now, yells about
two hours a day, but not yet at night, thank heaven. Sometimes I discern a little "ha," not really a call, only some sort
of social expression. It is already apparent that he likes company. How could I ever compare with Boel?

6-3. Anders has started to yell more; he has a loud voice and strong motions. He insists on food and company almost every hour of the day. A real pet he is. Everyone loves him.

6-6. Tries to lift his head when lying on his stomach, but his head drops down soon, and this makes him sad.

6-8. His smile has a more pronounced and livelier character.

7-11. Anders keeps his head up quite well now when he lies on his stomach. He laughs when anyone talks to him, "replies" with definite small gurgling sounds. He is awake more than before, yells a great deal but stops when anyone comes and talks to him. He does shadow-boxing when alone, enjoys lying free so he can look about. Out in the garden he lies on a blanket and watches the leaves move.

7-14. Anders is more and more accessible, awake, and interested; he is silent and listens when in company.

7-16. Today for the first time I hung a rattle over him—Boel's discarded silver rattle, and he already tries to hit it. He also studies with great interest the figures in an old nursery-room curtain we hang over his bed.

7-17. The rattle has calmed him; he yells much less.

7-24. He is now quite demanding, cries angrily when hungry, is growing fast, is interested in his surroundings. Complains if not allowed to lie free.

7-28. Anders laughs 'til he chokes; his laughing-sounds are much more "grown-up" than before.

7-29. Begins to "talk" to his mother, a string of "grrr—aaah —grrr—aah."

8-3. "Talks" more and more aloud to himself, and seems to enjoy the sounds. Seems to "answer" his own sounds. Laughs and wriggles in delight at contact.

8-29. Anders grows in beauty and wisdom. Now he gurgles for long periods. He has completely conquered the female members of the family.

"But why would you want to leave that little girl here—she seems quite normal. What a sweet child! The ones we have here aren't at all like that."

It was Emma, a nurse at the big institution we had considered. She tried to lead Boel by the hand, but Boel pulled
away each time and ran off on her irrational flights of discovery
from room to room, from bed to bed.

We had visited this institution earlier, several times. I had
"made myself familiar with the problem"; the day had now
arrived when I no longer could find excuses for delay—not
even my broken leg, which indeed was getting along quite well.

The delay had come to an end.

"You'll soon realize she isn't quite normal," I answered
guiltily. "She lives in a world entirely her own."

"So sweet she is!"

The nurse walked from bed to bed, from one room to another; greeted the children, patted them on the cheek, helped
one here, another there, comforting words. Her voice was low,
full of feeling, warm.

"They recognize me, every one of them, even those who
neither see nor hear very well. I love my little idiots, whether
they are sweet or not. Here is Boel's bed."

"Have you been here very long, Nurse?"

"Twenty-three years—I almost feel I'm one of them, perhaps I'm contaminated a little. But never mind—only stupid
people think the difference is so very great."

We had purposely waited until evening to take her there.
In that way the operation would be less painful, we thought.
Boel had run far down the corridor; she didn't turn to look
for us.

We drove home through the balmy summer evening; the
lush countryside seemed mockingly overripe—we had one
of the hottest summers in memory.

That night required many sleeping pills; the smoke screen
had finally disappeared.

Well, that was that summer.

Bengt had gone to America; the rest of our family had
moved out to our idyllic summer place at the long lake in

Sörmland, where night after night I raced through detective stories since no sleeping pills worked any longer. Now there was no need to run up and down hills searching for an escaped nomad, no need to lock doors, prepare separate meals, get up in the night, and clean up.

Boel was sitting in the same place each time when I came for my weekly visit. I had no opportunity to see her oftener, the institution was several miles north of the city, our summer place about eighty miles south. The two hundred miles back and forth was too much when the rest of the family needed me. Anders still had the breast, and I carried him with me in his basket on the back seat.

Unchanged and unchangeable Boel was sitting on her blue mattress on the floor of the nursery. She sat near the wall, alone among a great many children, her eyes riveted on the glass in the door. She would bang her head against the wall and stare at the door—dunk! dunk! During her seven years she had never shown that she recognized me any more than any of the others. Now, with her eyes on the door, I was barely over the threshold before she rose quickly. With careful steps she climbed over all her little feeble friends—this was a "calm" room, children with cerebral palsy and other immobilizing handicaps had been gathered together here, most of them lying or sitting on the floor. Her steps led directly toward the door. At once she took me by the hand, pulled me toward the entrance stairs, down the steps, out through the gate, to the car.

Now I had reason to remember all the times I had tried to analyze Boel's world of imagination. We had often said that she lacked ability to comprehend happenings outside a window—our kitchen window had long been our surest proof. How many times hadn't her father returned from work, stopped outside the big window and knocked—always without any sign of recognition or response from his daughter. How many times hadn't I driven the car down the hill, even aimed the lights through the kitchen window—without the slightest sign of reaction on Boel's part.

But here she was sitting, day after day, through the whole

week, waiting to see something through the glass door. For the first time she saw and seemed to comprehend what took place on the other side of a glass.

We had sometimes discussed the problem "mamma-preference" in connection with deaf children. Very often, in diagnosing a case, the first question would be: Has the child a definite mamma-preference? Both the remarkable dentist and the child-otologist considered this an important question. We had agreed that in this preference a great deal of the answer could be found as to whether or not the child had a usable mind, whether or not it was socially adjustable.

This, as we always said, was an essential factor in the child's general competence.

Boel had not had any special mamma-preference.

But now she sat throughout the week in her own imaginary world, in the large, beautiful nursery, and when her mother appeared on the other side of the glass door she rose with such lightning speed that one could hardly understand this quick reaction.

I would take her in the car.

On meaningless drives over highways and byways, Boel humming, I singing the same simple babble—"surr-surr-surr; Boel happy, surr-surr-surr, Boel likes the car. . . ." Sometimes we would leave the car, walk across some meadow. But then Boel's humming turned into a complaint, and we would return to the car, our steadfast friend—"Now we ride in the car, good car to ride in, good car, surr-surr-surr-surr! Boel likes car!"

Soon we had covered available roads, and we would drive back to the large, new institution, where, it seemed, the architects and the builders were ever in febrile activity, building new creations in brick, steel, glass, tile, and chrome.

Outside Boel's room the pipelayers were busy in their ditches. I remember especially one of them, a big, hefty man watching me with his gray, kind eyes. He made the same remark as Emma, the nurse, had made. And my reply to him was also tainted with a guilty conscience.

He said: "Why do you leave that little one here? She seems

completely normal to me, she doesn't belong here." And then he added: "Why don't you keep her at home? She ought to have a real home. And you ought to be ashamed of yourself!"

The big institution had only one fault—it was big.

Otherwise it had everything—it was light, comfortable, beautiful. For children who were "sociable" many possibilities existed. For a little "loneling" like Boel there was only a waiting for a face on the other side of a glass door. Among the children in her department none could eat or walk by themselves. This was an advantage, for Boel had more peace among these little ones than she would have had in some other department.

At the long formica-covered table in the dining room she sat all alone. Her greatest skill was in her eating. She had always handled herself well at table, never messing with her food—even though at times choosy—and had always reacted strongly against new items on the menu.

She sat there eating, and around her the aloneness was impressive and overwhelming. The child in the glass ball sat eating alone, and around her stretched empty, clean-washed formica surfaces, staring back at her like blank eyes. Tables at which no one else had a meal.

On the floor, the child in the glass ball was sitting on a blue mattress, and the long day was dunk-dunk against the wall, and an expectant look at the door.

The child was in the glass ball. Yet, at last, something had left the glass ball. Because the veiled look from her great, green-gray eyes under the heavy lids with their long, gold-fringed lashes was constantly directed toward something that before had meant nothing to her. It was directed toward a glass door behind which she waited to see someone appear. At last.

❧

I still keep in grateful memory all that was done to ease my steps. Humbly, even with a feeling of shame, I wish to express

141

my admiration for the institution's understanding doctors, its many good nurses, and gentle Emma whose life among her "little idiots" now has come to an end. Those eyes, seemingly colored by her surroundings, they did not blame me. They did not accuse me of ingratitude, in spite of all. They never accused me of anything, never. They looked beyond accusations and questions.

All of them were "good losers" that day when I came, my heart in my throat, and asked to get Boel back. I remember one of the young nurses, active among the Scouts, who could not hide her pleasure at seeing us drive off. I still can feel the warm handshakes of all of them, as much as to say: Hope all goes well! They were so effusive in their well-wishes I'll never forget them.

I don't believe my deep concern was apparent while I sat there and with a dry throat tried to explain and defend. The doctor and I had at least an hour's interview. He weighed for and against dutifully. A big, modern institution is a security that weighs heavily in the scales; I knew that. I also knew that the little white house which Inger had introduced me to did not offer nearly as great a security, in fact, none. I would exchange security for uncertainty—for something so unprotected as the little home which rested only on one woman's frail shoulders. Its brittle walls might crumble with the first storm, while the sturdy brick bastions of the institution would withstand the greatest hurricane.

And I knew that my worry for this good, delicate woman's life would now be my constant companion. Yet, this was what I wanted, and nothing else. I wanted a *home*. In spite of a vague assurance, with no promises attached, a trial as it were, I wanted this—home. I gave up all that security which perhaps represented wisdom, foresight, protection against all winds and weathers.

Perhaps this is what the child in the glass ball has taught me above all—to turn my back on misgivings that are so paralyzing, accept the day whatever it offers, and not worry about a future that might never come. Now I know it. Each day has its own sorrow. She has changed me, the child in the glass ball.

I wasn't sure as yet that a change in me was possible. We are all given our nature, are closed up in it, cannot escape it. I was missing this something so important—faith. Trust in Providence. Belief in the possibilities that—in spite of all —each new day brings.

I had so many plans—they always seemed so necessary; they couldn't be changed. Not so anymore. I no longer look to the future as other mothers, not in the same way. I no longer complain of the passing of time in the same way. No, at the end of each day I feel somewhat as I might at having a time-payment-account—the same diffuse feeling of relief at having made another payment before evening. And each morrow is a possibility without apprehension.

Thus, this child in the glass ball was to teach me this good lesson: no longer to lament the passing of time. The days are filled; they escape me quickly. But she has pointed to something more important, something greater—confidence in the new day's possibility. She has given me confidence in that God who has become mine.

To be two.

All human togetherness has its vicissitudes, its ups and downs, and between them perhaps the monotonous evenness that a field offers, a farmer's small field at the edge of a forest: much industry and little to show for it. All marriages have their happy moments, those to be remembered.

Every life has its periods of luminousness and those of fleeting grayness lacking contour. There will always be minutes, hours, days, or weeks which remain gilt-edged certificates, constantly increasing in value, in spite of constant inflation. There will also be those that slip into the past unnoticed, as if never having been, remain there, never to be recalled or tasted anew, never bitter-sweet forgotten.

Our marriage—judged superficially, thoughtlessly, with the

143

usual stereotype lack of imagination—might be called "happy," good, exceptional; all depending on who is the judge. Yet, it has encompassed the same changes as all others, and there have been shorter or longer periods which to me always will stand out as especially unforgettable—those rose-tinted, not-to-all-given. It is immaterial to me if I am wrong about this, if I be considered old-fashioned and naïve. I still own those moments, those periods.

Memory makes of them gilt-edged securities, permits me now and again to clip a coupon. When my purse is emptier than usual it is good to have this reserve. With a dwindling estate, with ever smaller dividends, those coupons might one day be my only assets; perhaps they will help me make debit and credit balance at last.

It is not my intention to enumerate those gilt-edged securities here; after all, this is no income declaration. No internal revenue service will examine it, and the undeclared items have not been omitted in order to falsify or mislead.

No, this is no self-declaration; it is the story of something entirely different. Yet, among the gilt-edged securities I must declare one. Of all the happy moments, I would like to present especially one, of free will, without regret over the increased tax that might be the result. I do it because that particular moment was destined to be a dividing point between two periods in our life, although at the moment we did not realize it as such.

Boel had now been sent to Ingeborg in the white house, the "home" I liked so well. The day I drove her there has often later seemed to me as one of the happiest in my life. It unfastened my many knots. It was on the twenty-third of September, fall was still as warm as summer; indeed, summer had been exceptionally dry and long.

September twenty-third.

In my diary for Anders there is so much happiness to be found around these dates.

9-20. Anders pulls himself up to a sitting position without the slightest trouble. He did it for the first time the day he was four months old, holding on to his mother's fingers.

144

9-24. Anders has started to play with his toes, roll over on his stomach, roll back again to play with his toes.

10-7. The first tooth arrived in Gothenburg where we had gone to meet Daddy, returning from U.S.A.

And now they are at hand, those valuable moments.

Father is returning from his long America journey; worry and shameful guilt during this long, lonely summer were over. Boel was well settled. Anders slept in his bed, in our hotel room in Gothenburg, satisfied after his first morning meal.

The quay was enveloped in thick, milky fog, sirens kept blowing from nowhere, stevedores kept yelling back and forth in their wonderfully clever Gothenburg dialect. I kept listening while staring out into the fog.

I had bought a new red coat.

Then—something was happening to the fog. The sun, pale and self-conscious, cool and white, broke down the fog curtain, pulled it gently apart. Out of the fog rose a bow—it seemed to me infinitely tall—a giant among the busy tugs that were dragging this heavy vessel to the pier.

The M/S Goonawarra took her time, crept in lazy caution through the oil-covered water. The voices grew in intensity —and then, then I discerned a figure on the bridge, talking to the captain. And he at last caught sight of my new red coat.

He was back. At last.

We were two again.

We had a week to ourselves—and to each other. In Troll-hättan we visited dear friends from our early, unworried youth. They kept talking of the new time we had ahead of us—with a new child! It was like reliving your youth! Wonderful, so clever we had been! They too had a latecomer in the family, somewhere in age between Riken and Anders.

I said to Bengt that evening: "How fortunate we are—we have four normal children—and each other. We can indeed be happy and satisfied."

"Of course!" said Bengt.

And yet, in that moment a feeling of apprehension came over me, as if suddenly I had been looking out over some dangerous depth which I had not noticed before or suspected. I added quickly: "I hope."

"How wonderful to drive on Swedish roads again!"
"Aren't all roads about the same?"
"None are like the Swedish! You feel you're back home again; they follow the contours of the landscape so softly, caressingly almost. The American roads are of course perfect. But so impersonal, so monotonous."
Our week was running out fast.

We drove through the autumn beauty of our country, followed the caressing roads wherever they led. Sometimes we would park the car in a clearing, walk through an unknown forest, hunt without plan for mushrooms.

But the summer had been dry, and where the silver-pale autumn sun glittered through among the trees we could not find a single edible mushroom peeking up in the heaps of yellow leaves and dry pine needles.

At times I would sit down on a stump and give the breast to Anders—it had a newly-married, youthful feeling in it to sit like that, in sensuous proximity to the earth, with the autumn blue canopy of heaven above.

I was very happy.

And the last few days of this all too short week melted away in our summer place in Sörmland. Fishing on the lake, walking through the woods, we had no premonition that this was a farewell to a much happier time than we had suspected.

❧

That fall brought a new interesting project that for a while made us forget the emptiness without our little girl. The Scout Association opened its new experimental school for higher education of talented deaf youths. Our good friend the director at the Institute for the Deaf had had to fight against much when he had advocated this form of higher education for the deaf. None of us who devoted our time to this project could know what we were in for, but he was more exposed to criticism than the rest of us. All we others needed was our conviction of the school's necessity; this we already had.

The little school could satisfy any desire for romanticism; it was situated at Blockhusudden, in an attractive Hansel-and-Gretel cottage looking out over one of the inlets to Stockholm, ever busy with sails and boating.

And our own home got a new guest to occupy Boel's bed.

Maja was fifteen and had deaf parents and brothers and sisters down in Borås. To offer one of the students at the Blockhusudden school a foster home with us seemed quite natural—in fact, we had "a room open" since Boel had left home. Our other children, the older ones, had never shown any irritation over Boel, their patience was endless. The babies were too little. When we discussed the possibility, Sten and Lena were at once eager to accept Maja in Boel's place.

The evening Maja arrived the older children were waiting, ready to receive her in the living room. Without a doubt they were filled with goodwill toward her. None of us could in advance have suspected the wall—so invisible yet unsurmountable—that would rise between this young girl and our children, hardened though they were from seven years' association with Boel and that world which lies beyond our realm of understanding.

Maja was happy and helpful, but she represented a new sort of incomprehensibility. More and more I came to realize how unreasonable it was to expect our children to comprehend this riddle. Sten was fourteen, himself in the same rebellion-against-everything-grown-up age as Maja. Lena was eleven, on the threshold of puberty. Both of them should have been left in peace.

I tried to explain: such was the deaf person's world; the rich stimulus to our imagination which sounds in various forms give to our consciousness was beyond Maja's reach—the chirruping birds in spring, rain against the window in fall, distant noise from a city, laughing voices from people on a beach in summer. Invaluable nuances which hearing people take for granted. Maja could hear none of this. In the severely

147

sober reality which limited her world she was denied the half-tones. Besides, she had to fight a battle beyond our comprehension to conquer a fraction of the natural tool of our thoughts, the language. The rest of us are handed this as a gift without effort.

True.

No one would contradict this. But—why must she forever "draw hasty conclusions from inconclusive evidence," to use a legal term so beloved by my father. Why must she always think wrongly?

I started over again.

Deaf persons are inclined to "overinterpret" every signal, have a more limited experience of what a signal, a word, an action might mean. They have such a narrow choice, so many fewer "alternative signals." Therefore they rush ahead and anticipate. They anticipate, and then they are deceived and confused when their interpretation turns out to be wrong.

True.

It was clear that it must be so. But—why was she so stupid at times, sulked at the smallest attempt to tease her? Didn't she have any sense of humor?

I tried again.

The sense of humor in a deaf child is much more direct. It is a sort of concrete comedy humor. Must remain so. We can't expect a deaf person to understand the nuances in a pun. The double meaning of a word, for example, how could that be understood? The amusing in a direct situation with comic meaning, however, is as easily understood by the deaf as by the hearing.

True—but. . . .

Maja once suggested that we avoid speaking to each other when riding the street car. Another opportunity for me to lament the cruel, conceited lack of understanding that everywhere confronts the deaf. A sweet, friendly young girl did not wish to be forced to experience this consequent reaction of puzzled, startled faces as soon as she let her voice be heard.

148

She would rather keep silent. And what could my inner anger do, except keep on and so I kept silent too.

Maja was at her happiest when she was caring for Anders—bathing him, feeding him, putting him to bed. Here she met neither impatience nor derison; Anders accepted her as she was. She loved him.

Maja still inquires about Anders when she sends us her Christmas and Easter greetings. She writes she would love to see him again. And I—I cannot reply, cannot explain to her. How could she understand what has happened to Anders?

The year Maja spent with us I learned a great deal. There was so much where I had expected nothing. And sometimes there was less when I had expected more. Her stay in our home thus became a problem on many planes.

I learned that limitations are always elastic, and the greatest wrong we can do the handicapped is to lock them in where we feel they ought to be.

The same year that Maja lived in our home a new activity was in progress in the Scout Association for the benefit of another group of handicapped children. We called it the "Light-Point." Its object was to take care of some of the needs usually overlooked among blind and partially seeing children. Here a whole new world opened—I had had very little to do with blind people before.

"Close your eyes a moment and think" was the slogan that met everyone everywhere during this campaign. The exhortation was not difficult to obey. It made one realize the slip-shod way in which we are accustomed to think. As far back as history records hasn't the blind man been surrounded with helping hands, endowed with supernatural wisdom, been given more than his share of sympathy? The deaf one, on the other hand, in olden days was considered possessed of an evil spirit; he looked like one of us, but he couldn't speak; or if he could talk, such strange sounds emanated from his throat that the breath of the evil one himself must have descended upon him.

149

The power of the word—again I would have reason to cogitate over this—the Word that was in the Beginning. Again the Inconvenient One stepped forward, with raised eyebrows perhaps, to pose an accusing question. And one day I asked this question to the dynamic leader of the blind—our friend since the start of the "Light-Point," himself blind since earliest childhood. He laughed a little, his typical wise and hearty laughter, spiced with a touch of irony:

"Yes, many people have asked that question—which would I prefer if I had had a choice from the beginning, whether to be deaf or blind? Perhaps I'm not the right one to answer that question, since I have experience only in one field. Yet my answer would be, without hesitation, I would choose to be blind. I have everything, in a way. Everything. I can travel wherever I wish, speak with everyone. I can imagine how everything looks. I'm not sure I imagine it correctly, but is this of any great importance? And what is right in that case? Is it so important that objects look exactly as you seeing people conceive them? And even among you you often see things differently, quite differently, isn't that so? What then is the difference? The great importance lies in enjoying things in a way only the individual can enjoy them. Who knows if it might not be as strong an experience to imagine what a red flower looks like as it is actually to see it? Do you know it? Of course it is a handicap to be blind, terribly difficult at times. But if I were forced to choose between sight and speech —never to have heard it or learned to use it, never to have built up one's language world, followed its lines of association —well, the answer could only be one."

Approximately in this way did he reply to me, that dynamic blind one.

And yet—I was myself to realize the absurdity of the very question. The deaf has his advantages; nothing shows in his appearance, he can participate with all on every occasion, he is not noticed. He must pay for his participation in that bitter coin: often to be un-understood, always misunderstood.

I was thinking of the time I had gone with Maja to the

150

station to see her off. There was an announcement about her train. All listened, were given information as to what to do— all except Maja. She did not react—she had heard nothing— and my apprehension was great as I helped her onto the train. Yet, she was barely behind her window, this sweet and attractive girl, before a young man in the same compartment was making eyes at her. Now she was neither misunderstood nor un-understood. At least there was this about it—she looked like others. The advantage of the deaf.

The blind again. This legend of old which endowed him with a superhuman wisdom—does he really possess it? Is it an advantage—or . . . ? Since the blind speaks as we do and is heard as others, one assumes that no shortcoming exists; he speaks as if he did see—he must then be endowed with supernatural powers. How could he otherwise—without the light of his eyes—know so much and be able to speak thus?

Another aspect: how often is a blind person forced to listen to others speak of him as if he weren't hearing. As if he weren't at all present, although close by. This is a crime we often commit—this, to speak of a handicapped one as if he were nothing but air. We commit it against the deaf, and particularly against the mentally retarded. We commit it against the maimed, we commit it against the blind who both hears and understands. This he endures in silence. Because he possesses tact and patience that is alien to us.

The first time I was at a Lucia-festival in an institution for the handicapped I had brought along Sten who was then fourteen years old. It would be more appropriate to say that I had insisted he come along—he had stated, more or less openly, that he considered a handicap in a child "disgusting."

After we had seen the children perform—many of them in wheelchairs or aided with crutches—decked out as Lucias, Santa Clauses, goblins, fairies—we were sitting at a long table enjoying our coffee and goodies. Across the table from Sten and me sat two elderly ladies, definitely of the "do-good" type. Next to Sten sat a little Lucia-attendant with withered legs, an inmate at the institute.

The conversation rose and fell, the coffee cups steamed, the candles fluttered. Presently my ear was caught by what the ladies opposite were talking about. One of them was saying that she recently had visited the institute for the blind, "those poor little blind critters" had had their Christmas party. The other spoke of the school for the deaf; and both had been to that new, big place and seen "those poor wretches that are so terribly behind." Soon they were in a lively argument, quite loud, as to which handicap would be the worst to be stricken with.

Sten and the little girl with unusable legs could not help hearing every word of the conversation. The girl, pale and serious, looked straight ahead of her. Sten looked sullen and repressed. And as for myself, I found it difficult to enjoy the delicious cookies.

Suddenly Sten exploded, to my great astonishment:

"We had a sharp Lucia-feast at our school today; you should have seen our Lucia! This one here doesn't come near her by a long shot! She came from the girls' school at Sveaplan, the best-looking in the whole bunch! And she brought along a whole troop of attendants, everyone a real looker; and we could eat all the candies and cakes we wanted, and no one stopped us, and then the Lucia caught fire—the candles on her head dripped down on her costume—and her hair was full of paraffin. A terrible blaze it was before they got it out. And one boy had a saxophone, and he blew the music to Lucia on the pyre; he did it swell. A heck of a good party— the girls wouldn't even leave until we. . . ."

I tried in vain to signal Sten to stop. Didn't he realize how unsuitable it was to brag to a lame little girl about all that his healthy friends had been able to do at his school? I was looking about irresolutely—when my eyes came to rest on the little girl with the lame legs.

Her appearance had changed completely. Her eyes were shining, hanging on to Sten's story with glittering rapture; the color had risen to her cheeks, she was enjoying it. Gone were the old ladies, gone all sighs, all expressions of misery. She was elated.

And there I was sitting with my busy worry. I had wanted to spare her. She did not want to be spared at all. She wanted to live in this like any other girl—a boy at her side bragging about his escapades. She wanted nothing better than just to sit there and listen. Jealousy was not a part of this; she only wanted—in true feminine fashion—to sit and admire an individual of the male sex, without reservation. And without any logical reason. Exactly as each one of us wants, we women.

Sten had not read any psychology. But he taught me something essential, without himself being conscious of it. We speak so much of equality these days. Don't we nearly always mean, sometimes with appalling precision, a material equality? The same salaries, same educational opportunities, same material benefits? In a thousand ways, that is what our discussions are about. And yet—there is a much more important equality, perhaps the most important of all—the right not to be treated with humiliating pity.

"Wretch." The word itself implies a danger.

The "Light-Point" was to open my eyes better than anything to the danger in the word wretch. The blind child is born to compassion, the helping hand is ready. Every minute it will be there, ready. I had never thought about how dangerous this is. The conception "overprotection" now became a new reality. To be viewed from many perspectives.

And while the "Red Knot" had brought the important message to fathers and mothers that they should interest themselves in their children, try to do things for them, and be close to them constantly with explanations and words, so now the "Light-Point" was to teach mothers and fathers almost the opposite: not to aid their little ones in everything; let them find out for themselves, stimulate them to get along by themselves, avoid using exaggerated—and thus hurtful—consideration. I learned it had happened that little seven-year-old blind children had been brought to the institute without having acquired the ability to eat or dress themselves. Passive, without initiative, they came. But then, why should a child who sees nothing—and consequently lacks that stimulus to move which the sight of a distant object means to us who see—why should it move at all when it is easier to listen to the world around it?

These were new angles of approach to consider, new enemies to fight. The sector of the problems had widened.

IX

"Are you worried about Anders?"

"A little perhaps. And you?"

"Yes, I too. I don't know exactly why."

"Nor I. But it's something. . . ."

Anders was lying in his bed on the balcony taking his afternoon nap; a funny little snub nose, rosey cheek, hair turning white-blond. A child exposed to more observations than most.

"I had better take him to a doctor."

"What could he say? There is nothing definite."

"Only our apprehensions."

"Well, what could the doctors say, beyond what we know? Better wait and see."

However, at last I went with Anders to see our friend the child-otologist. With me also was an increasing fear, as yet rather formless and indefinite.

"Something is wrong—only I don't know what. Nothing like Boel. They are not in the least alike. But something. . . ."

"Come, Anders!" The otologist was calling our little boy who was conducting a private examination of the room, stamping along a little unsteadily, leaning against walls, holding on to chairs.

Anders stopped at once, turned his head, let go of his hold, and sat down on his behind and started crawling toward us.

"Nonsense! Look for yourself!" said my friend. "He both hears and reacts like any normal child. Mothers like you are impossible! Full of notions! Go home and be ashamed of yourself!"

※

That spring—besides my other studies—I took what was called a test-course at the university. Then I tested Riken and Lena, read the authorities on the subject—Gesell, Bülow, Ekman among others—and placed Anders' functions in the squares where they belonged. His skill at rising upright, walking, discriminating, reacting to certain simple stimuli—all this lay within the borders of normalcy, as far as one can measure such a small child's reactions. But there was one factor I could not get away from.

He had a peculiar way of grabbing with his right hand. In some way he didn't use his fingers; he would pick up an object with the palm of his hand, and he didn't hold it the way a one-year-old does. He simply dropped it from the palm of his hand. His left hand, when he used it, did not function in that way.

I pursued all the "right-hand functions" in Anders—there was no doubt that in some way they were different from those of a right-handed child. I spoke to a new doctor about it, related my observations of the spasms or contractions during Anders' very early days. I also told him that I thought his right-hand functions were in some way more passive than his other functions.

"I suppose he is left-handed then," said the doctor. "What's the difference?"

"He isn't left-handed," I replied.

"How do you know?"

"I can see it. He is learning to be left-handed. And that means he will have trouble with his speech."

"Pure imagination, I would say!"

How many times during this period didn't I hear that it was my imagination. That I had stared myself blind at Boel. That the variation was so great. Among a hundred children there were so and so many. . . .

"But we must compare with our own children—not with a hundred children from two hundred parents! We must compare with his normal brother and sisters. Isn't this the correct thing to do? They have the same parents, the same surroundings."

As spring waned I tried to suppress my worry; Riken was such a busy and funny little "mother"—the two of them played so well together. And so many other happenings took place to make me forget my apprehension.

My father died in April, which left me to take care of Mother.

Sten suddenly quit school and went to work. Now new worries assailed me: had I neglected the other children too much?

Later I was to learn that Sten's interrupted studies were only to the good, that he needed a time to grow and decide for himself. Nor did he get any serious scars from his adventure, except that his marks in gymnastics, drawing, and music were absent when he later graduated from high school. But that spring and summer I had a guilty conscience about the healthy children, and it would be untrue to deny that I was very happy the day Sten decided to go back to school. He himself gave me a crushing rebuke when I tried to see his approach to education and free will:

"Nonsense, Mother! You should never have gone in for psychology—it's written by old men and women who only think they have been young once upon a time!"

❧

"Vrena, July 27.—Forgive me for not writing earlier, but my summer has been so terribly broken up. First our place in the

157

country was flooded, and we had to shift about a lot. Then I unexpectedly had to go to Stuttgart with a relative of mine. However, I hope you never doubted you would hear from me sooner or later—it was after all a promise.

"I have been thinking about your series of radio programs and would make the following suggestions: for deaf children it would be desirable to have two separate programs, one for totally deaf, and one for the hard of hearing with usable residual hearing. The interview with the father of the totally deaf boy could be combined with a visit to the Institute for the Deaf to give the father opportunity to speak about the deaf child's most important problem—its education. The Scout Association's new school for theoretical instruction for the gifted deaf—where the boy now is a pupil—could also be visited, to let the boy himself express his opinion. You could let your audience listen to one of their English lectures over the radio—I have listened to their excellent English myself and think this would be most instructive. Perhaps the program could be rounded out with an appeal for equal right to education for the deaf as for those with normal hearing; also an appeal to widen the choice of vocation, to equalize somewhat with opportunities offered to normal Swedish youth of today.

"The mother of the hard of hearing child we spoke of—the one who has some residual hearing—could tell about her work with the boy, how she started when he was only two years old. She has tape-recordings of his earliest attempts to speak; this would be fine to add to the interview. He has gone through the preparatory school for hard of hearing children, in fact, the Scout organization started the school in her very home; now it is run by the city of Stockholm. A visit there would be very rewarding. The boy now attends the hearing class of the city schools. A visit to this class would also be interesting, and you might relate examples from the excellent instruction there.

"I have made an outline for my own program, suggesting two sections: one on the purely personal plane—you did ask for personal impressions, didn't you—and one concerning principles? I'll mention a few points that might give you some idea:

158

"1. Apprehensions and presentiments. 2. The importance of speech. 3. The pursuit of symptoms and causes. 4. Attempts to explain it away. 5. The blessing in not at once getting the whole truth. 6. A few characteristic samples in the behavior of the retarded child. 7. At home or away? 8. The separation from the child. 9. The big institution, a mother's nightmare. 10. The small home, the parents' demand.

"When you reach the point where I speak of the 'good-will-chain-reaction', i. e., when I explain how I found a home for our daughter, Boel, through the help of a good woman, you might make a visit to Boel. And wouldn't it be well to ask a few questions from the owner of this home? Why she plays those simple, stimulating records, like 'Mayor Munthe, Rode his Brunte etc.' for the children?

"For it is my hope we may be able to get two of the children to sing, even though they might not begin promptly. It is a very strange and moving song they produce. Perhaps you might even catch the voice of little Ake whose talk is continuous, though his conversation is limited to a few questions. He might say, perhaps a score of times: 'Are you Boel's mamma'? but that wouldn't matter, do you think?—With kindest greetings, Karin Junker."

I went to Klövsjö for three weeks in August, then we journeyed to Holland in September. That fall was to be rich in happenings. It passed; even winter was almost over when at last, in March the following year, the radio program about Boel was presented, the first in a series concerning handicapped children. The program was handled by a capable, warm-hearted woman with broad understanding; she spared no effort in making herself familiar with every side of the problem confronting a mother with a child who "isn't like others."

One side of the problem, however, escaped her. Actually, she could not have known about it. No one except I myself knew anything about it.

She did not suspect, could not know, that I during those days again relived the anxiety; more painful and intense, more bitter, entirely different yet so familiar, so related, new and horrible, and yet so old.

When I much later spoke to her about Anders she replied —and it struck me like a box on the ear: "Well, you can take it. You can take what you get. I just feel you can."

At first I could not understand how she could speak so, but by and by—after she had explained her conviction that "those that have broad shoulders can carry heavy burdens"—then I understood. And I realized also what a challenge she had presented to me; and how dear it would be to cultivate.

I had been given the finest compliment anyone ever has given me. I was not worthy of it; I do not know if I ever can measure up to it. The only thing I can do is to try.

"To part is to die a little"—this is one of the many expressions whose truth the heart repeats without urging, in spite of its banality. *Partir, c'est mourir un peu.* I am experiencing that very feeling of loss as an ache in my joints: it might be a deadly pain just as well as a short, passing misery. But it is there, however I describe it—that longing, that pleasing joy, that smarting pain, all at the same time.

I have just accompanied Lena to the train, my girl, our daughter. She is gone and has left me alone with my papers and my memories in a room that now is strangely empty. Just before she left she read the manuscript of my book, while I watched her beautiful eyes, listened to her soft voice, noticed the knitted brows when she recognized familiar scenes.

And now I am sitting in my lonely hotel room, crying. Outside wet branches brush against the window, gray clouds are gathering, busily. I am crying over the short moments, the intimate and inexpressible ones which never return, because they lie in the nature of moments gone.

What is a girl—a daughter—during those years when she hasn't as yet stepped across the threshold to the realities of our gray, everyday life? When questions reveal tell-tale secrets, when every happening is filled with expectation? Who was it that borrowed one's last nylon stocking when I myself was in need of it? Who spilled nail polish over the dresser? Who used my only dress-up blouse, my new walking shoes? Who found my hidden cigarettes, used my face lotion before I had time to replenish it?

But to have someone who listens and wants one to listen also: to explain what this means to a mother like me with a child in a glass ball is not only difficult, it is impossible.

To me it is sufficient once in a while to sit together, as Lena and I have just done, only the two of us, at a dinner table in a hotel in a strange place, talk small talk, feel festive and serious at the same time, exchange thoughts on serious matters and laugh at inconsequentials, all in the same breath. There is a communion between us that flows freely, without effort, as we sit talking over the coffee, a communion in which both of us are conscious of the difference in age—without complaint, regret, or bitterness; to us it is not an abyss that we must spend our strength in overcoming, it is only the natural distance in years, quite acceptable.

I had wanted to ask her forgiveness for neglect I had not intended. I had wanted to confide in her how it hurt me to miss any possibility that moments like these give me. And yet —I might never have utilized the possibilities any better even if none of the misfortunes which had struck us had been absent. What can I know about such matters? All around me I see so many thrown-away opportunities, so many mothers and daughters, so many high walls, so many cold looks, so many clefts of misunderstanding and intolerance. Who can say it would have been different between us if we had been in their shoes? Who can say that and be sure? Not I, not Lena.

But now.

We have our moments, rare, good, in our way, as mother and daughter; without a silly pretension of being sisters, a pretension destined to disintegrate sooner or later. And so— forgive me if for a moment I have interrupted my story to enjoy this ounce of irrational nostalgia before I return to my tale. Return to the weak.

The ninth of March fell on a Saturday that year. The radio program had been given space during the most desirable hour in the evening. My friend Inger and I had decided to listen together; she had come to our home and was sitting on the double sofa in front of the fire, her slender legs crossed, her chin resting against her delicate hand. Our eyes met in suspense as we heard my voice over the radio, so alien yet familiar:

" . . . I know it sounds superstitious when I say I knew in advance something would happen to our little girl. Yet it was so. It is not something invented afterwards."

This was indeed a new kind of Saturday evening program. I caught myself admiring the courage of the radio woman.

"Gradually I got accustomed to having a reply ready when people came with questions. Why did Boel act so strangely? Why did she do this, or that? I had an answer ready—and in a way it was as if I had believed in my answers. Yet the realization grew within me, on the sly as it were, that there was something wrong about them. It was during the period when we went from doctor to doctor, an experience so familiar to parents with developmentally disturbed children. We tried different theories, we hunted for causes, turned in and out every incident that had taken place, every neglect we felt guilty of. . . .

"Now, afterwards, I realize the blessing of not knowing the whole truth at once. There are so many peculiarities in a developmentally inhibited child that it is easier to learn gradually and get accustomed to. . . . I was convinced I would never separate Boel from our home in those early years; I didn't want to hear the thought of it even. I remember the thought did come to me sometimes—perhaps it would be best if we both were to die. Occasionally I thought Boel might have an accident which would end her life, and we would never need make a decision about her future.

"We decided to send Boel away, partly because of our healthy children; we did not wish them to grow up under the burden of constant consideration for a mental invalid. Partly

162

for Boel's sake; we wished to secure her future. We said many times—who can tell how long we might live? Suppose we have an accident, and nothing is arranged for Boel. The other children, being healthy, would manage in some way. But Boel was helpless, completely helpless. We must, while there was time, seek protection for her. . . . I do not hesitate to say it was a gift from heaven the day I learned that Boel could stay in a small home. It was another mother, of another retarded child, who . . ."

Inger and I exchanged glances. Then she lowered her eyes in her usual modest sort of way and seemed to inspect the sharp toes of her shoes.

". . . in every way helped me get in contact with the home where her daughter is. Thus I have had personal experience in how important is the contact between parents in our situation. Boel is now in this little home; there are altogether only five children there. The daily rhythm is identical with that of a normal family. I have with my own eyes observed how Boel gradually adjusted herself to a daily routine that has given her a greater feeling of security and made her happier and more in harmony with her surroundings. Yes, I almost believe Boel is happy now."

After we had listened to "Mayor Munthe, Rode his Brunte" and the modest owner's shy answers when interviewed by the radio woman, we sat for a long while in silence and thought. Then I told Inger of my conversation with the doctor at the big institution the time when I went after Boel. I related what I had said:

"I don't know how they do it, these anthroposophists, nor what it means, this Waldorf-pedagogy which they follow, but it is quite clear they have something to teach us, something very important—only, I don't know what. They have succeeded with so much where we mothers have failed. Undoubtedly they too have failed in some respects, as have we all, but the fact remains that they radiate an atmosphere of faith, a conviction about every child's possibilities, which we cannot afford to ignore.

"Obviously I'm not naïve enough to imagine that an official

institution can be based on certain religious beliefs, or even should be, but I don't think we can get along without those people who are willing to devote themselves—through inner conviction—to our developmentally inhibited, be they anthroposophists, ordinary Christians, or simply idealists. We cannot get along without them, we cannot manage alone. The most important—the personal involvement—is so easily lost in the well-oiled machinery of a large institution. We must be particularly anxious to contact people personally involved."

Well, that was how I had expressed myself that time.

Inger and I went to the kitchen and prepared a few sandwiches for ourselves.

We both knew that much discussion went on among parents, as to whether or not it was right to send away a child, or if—at any price—it must be kept at home. Neither one of us could answer that question. I told about one young doctor I had met who had said he never could forgive his parents for allowing him to grow up with his retarded brother. All the time that retarded boy must participate in everything; in every situation in which the young doctor was involved. I had heard of other examples, and in each case the parents had been mistaken, either in the eyes of the other children, or the handicapped child, or the neighbors.

How could I answer the question? How could Inger? There was no always-right answer, never. There are a thousand pieces in the puzzle that must fit together. The variations in different children's equipment is so great—some are easier, others more difficult to take care of, some understand their situation, suffer more than others from a separation from home. Some don't suffer at all.

A child is always best off at home, some will say. Others say it is a crime to sacrifice the harmony in an otherwise healthy family. The surest advice is always given by those who never have personally met the shadows of the picture.

But the choice must always be a strongly personal one, we felt that evening as often before. And those whom society has put in a position to aid us in these matters, they must realize this. Their duty is not to offer patronizing advice, tainted with rebuke, their duty is to aid, comfort, help. It has happened that parents have called me in despair, because— lacking in enthusiasm for some suggested placement—they had been told they should have been grateful.

"To whom shall we be grateful?" they have asked me. "Shall we thank God he has given us a child that is unlike others? Or shall we thank the authorities?"

We talked much and long about this over the warm sandwiches in our kitchen that evening. One question is also, we agreed, how to manage to live on—with or without the child. One had to consider that viewpoint too.

I had no patent solution to that question. I only knew something about my own experience. It was that I must seek a concrete task, turn outward, find my way to all the others. Otherwise I could not endure. I must live, not vegetate. I had an answer: to live, fully and completely, to try to take from the stores that perhaps were mine, and distribute as much of them as I could.

But a solution for all I did not have. Nor did Inger. To this day I have not found one.

"Mrs. Junker insists we make a psychiatric examination of the boy," said the pediatrician at the children's hospital with a gesture of despair. His sad eyes indicated a certain surrender; perhaps he hadn't encountered this type of persistence before.

It was autumn and nothing of what I have related above had as yet taken place. We had just returned from Holland to find Anders gone. He had got a cold with high fever. During our absence Anders had been taken care of by our maid, while a relative of ours, who also was Anders' godmother, acted as family advisor. Before we had left Anders had recovered from croup, and we had instructed our relative to contact our friend the child-otologist in case a doctor was needed. Now Anders was at the big university hospital, where his temperature-curves and the noise in his chest were being studied and taken care of.

So my opportunity had come all by itself. The doctor said: "There is really no reason to keep him here any longer— except that your wife wants him here. The temperature went down long ago, his tubes sound very good, the X rays show nothing. No reason why you shouldn't take the boy home. He is completely recovered."

It almost sounded as if the doctor were appealing to Bengt to take Anders home. This was Authority speaking, and Bengt was undecided as to what to do. "Don't you think we should examine his mental functions?" he suggested.

"Frankly, no. We have had him under observation here at the clinic—Mrs. Junker has been so insistent about this—but I must honestly say I believe it's pure imagination. Nothing unusual about a child being a little slow in starting to talk."

"But, Doctor," he managed to say, "we have another child who is mentally retarded."

"Precisely," he said. "We have so much more to compare with here; we can much better decide the scope of variation. There is nothing abnormal in Anders' development, nothing that doesn't come within the frame of normal variation."

I no longer had the strength to point out that the range of variation among brothers and sisters with the same parents ought to offer a much more reasonable basis for comparison. I only said, tiredly: "After all, he is my fifth child. I have actually studied these matters, more or less. I have seen a great deal. I'm daily in contact with children with various handicaps, as well as with their mothers."

"Well—I've only expressed my opinion. I consider it unnecessary to keep the child here at the clinic when there is no need for it," said the doctor, now in a definitely short tone of voice.

Bengt looked at me with a wavering question in his eyes: perhaps it would be just as well . . . ? Suddenly my fatigue was gone, I straightened up my shoulders:

"I insist you make a thorough psychic examination of him!"

166

I said. "Find out as much as you can now while he still is here in the hospital. If not, as soon as you can."

In my mind I already anticipated a vague excuse about long waiting lists, but I hoped that the doctor's sad eyes would weaken, and that he also would realize the practicability of killing two birds with one stone—not discharge Anders and have to accept him later.

He realized this. There was no mention of waiting lists.

❧

"Well, we have not been able to discover a thing. We've actually exhausted all possibilities," said the doctor with the sad eyes. "Nothing unusual. Being so little he doesn't talk, and so it's difficult to obtain the same contact as it will be later. Let's see—how old is he? A year and a half, not quite. You can't expect much. We have kept him under observation —there is nothing definite to get hold of. We have also made certain tests, all negative."

"Have you noticed how he handles objects when he uses his right hand?"

"Many children act that way—it doesn't mean a thing."

We had both been asked to come to the clinic—perhaps the doctor wanted male support against my obstinacy.

"Well, now we can take Anders home, then," said Bengt, relieved.

"As I say, I have nothing more to add. I can't see the slightest reason for concern. He is a healthy, fine boy, and if he should be down a little just now it's only what could be expected after a high fever and being in the hospital. It's never good for children to be in hospitals—they always go down then."

We had already risen to leave; I believe we had even shaken hands when I said: "And what about the electro-encephalogram? What did it show?"

"To tell the truth, we didn't take one." The doctor looked surprised. "There was hardly any reason for one, as far as we could see."

I remained nailed to the floor: suddenly this seemed more important than anything else. I simply didn't want to leave the hospital until I had definite information about this. I said:

"I wish you would take one while he is here." And now I added, with more firmness than I thought I possessed: "I am quite convinced that something is wrong with Anders even though I realize one cannot see much in such a small child."

"But . . . an electro-encephalogram at this age . . . one can't expect it to indicate anything. When he has no spasms or . . ."

"Please, take one, Doctor!"

We left the hospital with much easier steps than when we had arrived; both of us felt almost exhilarated.

"There, you see!" said Bengt. "All in your imagination! Let's go out and have a good dinner!"

And the dinner turned out to be really good. It was also a sort of improvised farewell dinner for Bengt—again he was to go away somewhere for some time.

We left the restaurant in high spirits.

Two days later a nurse called from the hospital.

"The doctor would like both of you to come up here this afternoon," she said.

"Both of us? My husband has gone away—must we wait 'til he gets back? Why does the doctor want to talk to both of us?"

The nurse sounded reticent. "The doctor only told me to say that he wanted to talk to both of you."

"But I am alone now."

"Well, better come alone, then, Mrs. Junker," she said, and named the hour.

I felt very much alone as I walked into the doctor's office. He was sitting at a plain desk; his beautiful, sad eyes had lost all their lustre since I had last seen him. It was, in some way, as if he had shrunk, collapsed. He asked me to sit down. There was a short silence.

"Well," he said at last with a sigh, "you were right, Mrs. Junker. All is not well with Anders. You were indeed right."

"You mean—the electro-encephalogram?"

"I mean—it was as you suspected."

I had known right along.

I cannot say I was struck by lightning, that it was an unexpected shock, or whatever one calls it. I had, after all, known.

And at once it seemed as if our roles had changed, as if I should have comforted the doctor rather than the reverse. I suddenly seemed to have a big, sad boy on my hands, whom I in some way had cheated or caused to be disillusioned. When I spoke it was almost as if trying to cheer him up.

"I suspect that something happened to him during my operation—when he wanted to be born but couldn't make it?" I rambled on, even succeeded in making my voice steady.

"Probably," he said softly.

"Perhaps some injury, some small brain hemorrhage, for example, or perhaps some interruption in the nutrition supply during anesthesia? Or perhaps lack of oxygen? Or . . ."

"It's very possible. . . ."

"He has a definite under-function in his whole right side, don't you agree, Doctor?" I said, with growing animation. "He grabs so strangely with his right hand, uses the palm. The fingers on that hand are so inactive—I felt it might indicate something wrong with the left side of the brain, perhaps some hemorrhage? When I began noticing it I suspected at once that something might be wrong with his speech-development. He will not use his right hand if he can help it."

"But he is definitely not left-handed!" exclaimed the doctor, he too with growing animation. "He has no definitely marked left-hand preference. On the contrary, he is right-handed."

"Yes," I said, and now it was I who sounded sad, "he is right-handed, and that is the problem. Had he been born left-handed, then I wouldn't have worried about his right side. Nor about the development of his speech."

This time there was a long silence.

In some way the sad doctor looked embarrassed, as if he had been caught red-handed. Embarrassed—but also tired. And I—I too felt suddenly very tired. Suddenly I saw myself from the outside—with the diagnosing doctor's eyes.

I saw myself as an importunate, irresponsible busybody—one of those annoying mothers who had read entirely too much, and yet not enough. Because books had not always been available; because all books had an end, all sentences ended with a period. Because books are books in spite of all; they are not life, the trembling, suffering, inexplicable, and frail.

And in truth I am a time-consuming mother.

Perhaps my reasoning might be logical enough—per se—but I see lucidly and with a peculiar feeling of fatigue, that in reality I don't know the first thing about these matters, about "co-ordination between speech-centrum and right-hand-function," about the danger of "damage to the fetus with anesthesia," about preferences here and preferences there. I cannot know this. Speculations within the framework of yard-long shelves of books in psychology and physiology—perused during long, lonely vigils in my first-floor cubicle—these do not give me the answer from which to draw strength, to stick to, or follow. No one knows enough in these matters to offer a prognosis of enduring value. Every year new discoveries are made, new hypotheses are brought forth, concerning this fascinating mechanism—the human brain, the central nervous system. Each new year brings a new hue-lit hope in its bosom.

But each year also brings forth individuals who are not caught in the hypotheses, who persistently poke fun at them by unostentatiously ignoring the statistics, the "reliable" columns, the tables—by seeking the untried, unlighted fields beyond. And each year the old hopes are extinguished anew.

Suddenly I see it so clearly!

Why do we look at the little child who didn't get to be like all the others, who happened to be a break in the beautiful pattern of uniformity, why do we look at it in another way than we look at a flower or an insect that didn't happen to be like its neighbors? Suppose in spring I should walk through a field of bowing cowslips—heavy, honey-fragrant clusters in the rain-strewn grass. Perhaps I would stoop and pick a sweet-smelling spring bouquet—I would choose the biggest, the heaviest, the richest in honey.

But I would also see here and there a stunted plant, and not so few either, with a shorter stem, smaller blossoms, fewer blooms in the clusters, some even malformed. This would not surprise me.

No, I'm not in the least disturbed by these little half-hidden plants, although, for the purpose I have in mind, I pick calmly and methodically the biggest, the strongest—no statistics bother me during this spring walk through the wet grass of a May evening.

But I would never think to reject the small plants, even the deformed ones. I would never think that the field was less beautiful because of them. Nor would I harbor dislike, contempt, or repugnance—much less disgust—because of these little malformed or crippled cowslip-children. They have their place—a natural, definite one—just where they stand there in the grass, in the midst of all the others.

Why need it be different in the world we call our own, the human world? Why couldn't we in the same way accept a few deviations in the great multitude, a few doomed to be crippled, yet doomed to life. And this brings to mind something one of my good friends once said—he works in the field of biology, especially zoology; he has studied dandelions and is now an authority in genetics. What he said was as follows:

"We think of it as terribly strange if something is wrong with a human individual, but accept without hesitation as quite natural that something is wrong with a certain percentage of all other living individuals—flowers, animals, fishes, insects—mention what you will. Isn't this a ridiculous position? In all other forms of life we acknowledge this simple biological law—only in the case of human beings do we object and protest. I feel that the logical consequence should be that we all accept responsibility for this natural distribution among humans which exists in all other species. In our family circle we have altogether about twenty-five children—I happen to be the one given the defect sample. It was quite natural that

171

some one among us should get it, just a blind chance made me the father to this exception. But all of us have the same responsibility toward this deviation. *Exactly the same!* It is this, and only this, that is at the root of the question or fact—that we all share in the responsibility for a law of nature which concerns all of us."

To go back to my interview with the doctor; it was no longer of particular importance. We talked, back and forth, rather irresolutely about a number of practical details which I knew were of little consequence. Because this was no longer a medical problem; in fact, most problems with handicapped children are less medical than we are inclined to think. The medicine men have their halos, because it must be so, has always been so. But—the effort, the struggle through long days and years, the effort to bring the injured plant its optimal chance for growth, lies in nine of its ten parts on another plane.

It lies on the plane of education—to express it like that is another projection. It is an expression capable of hiding the eternally daily disappointments, the insolubility of the many equations concerning the defective plant, its care, its attention in days to come.

The halo of the medical man covers the one tenth which, in spite of all, perhaps is necessary. The other nine-tenths might hardly come to happen without it, nor could we mothers endure without these "beautiful years of illusion." Could we keep on breathing without the life-giving oxygen of illusion?

I would therefore—just therefore—have liked to give the sad doctor across from me some comfort of greater potency. I would have liked to say something that sounded like gratitude, acknowledge his patience in doing as I wanted, some sort of homage to him and all in his profession. Something to make him understand that I knew something about this, and had accepted it as part of a necessary whole, that I knew the limitations, so inflexible, so inexorable.

But I said nothing of all this. Instead, I said, perhaps with a touch of suppressed arrogance:

"Doctor—how could you be so sure that I was wrong?"

172

He looked up, a quick blush over his face:

"Lightning seldom strikes twice in the same place."

My last question, as I rose to leave, was only for the sake of formality: "And now? What should we do now? What do you think, Doctor, that we should do with Anders?"

This time the silence was long.

When at last he replied, he shrugged his shoulders in a gesture of utter powerlessness:

"You know better than I."

X

I knew best what to do, the doctor had said. But—all was so different this time, so unlike Boel. It was different, and yet too familiar. This the doctor could not know.

The "Värmland Pine" had had a program, and she was the type who would follow it. I had for a few years pretended I followed a similar program. Many, many of the mothers of blind children whom I had met could do the same; they could face their problem from the very beginning, follow their particular program.

Not so for me. I could only wait.

Anders was a sweet, towheaded little baby—friendly, open, well-developed, eager for contact. His word supply consisted of sounds for thank you, look, mamma, pillow, doggy—phonetically easy to identify.

But I hardly needed any "Authority" to tell me that a systematic speech training might be directly damaging. In cases

174

of disturbance in the motor-speech-function—or in any other motor-function (the passiveness in blindness might be considered another motor-disturbance)—in such cases there is at least the comforting possibility for the mother that she can follow a definite training program. Every activity helps because it produces a change. In motor-damages it is the *motion* that points to the future and the cure.

I knew that my lot in waiting was nerve-wearing. A central speech disturbance has little to do with motor-speech-disturbance. Speech and language are two different things, a fact I would come up against again. In the case of Anders—suffering from central-speech-disturbance—I could only wait for what we call ripening to maturity. No hothouses exist in which to place a child like Anders for "forced ripening," as one does with tomato plants. The distraction and comfort a mother has in having to train something or someone in the forward movement was not for me.

I must wait; not a silent, indolent waiting, without stimulants—rather, a waiting without hothouse aid or forcing fertilizer. Without a program.

It was a difficult waiting.

And while it lasted I came up against many problems in other fields which I must try to solve according to my ability. My mother, after Father's death, had to look for a new place to live. An old, once well-to-do home must be broken up; we had to find a little apartment for Mother somewhere; my childhood home destroyed.

One memory still chokes me: Mother on her knees in the room where I was born; stricken by a fate that had been harder than most people's, finally forced to leave this beautiful bedroom with its lofty balcony and magnificent view over Stockholm and its harbor.

The moving men, as always, had been in a great hurry, and every chair had been removed, leaving only the bare floor. Mother's dear old worn hands poking and digging in a pile of junk in the middle of the oak floor, searching among photographs of long-forgotten friends of her youth, broken trinkets, bunches of keys, small jars and bottles of once important medi-

175

cines, tools and knick-knacks. She must, in her great eagerness, have been searching for something definite, her face a mold of panic and pain.

I urged her to hurry—because I must. I must hurry, I must tear her away from all these memories that dragged her down, down. I had myself fought with this emotional moving, until my bad leg started to ache, until I suspected I might need another operation. My youngest brother had emigrated to Canada, leaving a painful vacuum that none could fill; my oldest brother had long been an American citizen; my next oldest brother was stationed in Lappland. I alone had been left behind, alone I must demolish this old colorful home.

Soberly and with a matter-of-fact attitude, so alien to me, I forced myself to say:

"Forget all that junk, Mother! I'll rake it together and put it in the garbage can tomorrow. Come now, let's go!"

Mother lifted her head and looked at me. She had an expression of infinite loss, a loss for something that only seemed to have been, but never was.

"You don't know what you're talking about, girl," was all she said.

She was late in arriving, this woman doctor. Her office was dark, old-fashioned. A pale, black-haired girl disappeared somewhere in the interior; two patients were sitting on a sofa, talking in low voices. They did not seem to be in a hurry.

Anders was very busy—the floor offered space, the walls echoes. Time passed. The dark-haired girl returned from her mysterious hiding place in this sea of big rooms. She stopped interestedly before Anders, began to talk to him, prattled a little as girls will do with boys of that size. She had an accent but not more than to make it attractive.

Perhaps it was the fashion in these circles, that one sat waiting. The peace was absolute, no signs of rush, no tension in the air during this silent, almost endless waiting. Minutes were added to minutes, grew into an hour, into two.

At last there was a rattling of keys; someone was coming.

No hurry, no invented excuses.

I held Anders firmly by the hand as we entered her private office. This time I would not show my "great knowledge"; I had decided that the listener's role this time would be played by me. I had gone through this business so many times that I no longer had anything to say. I was getting tired of talking.

I had no information to offer, no journals or diaries, no hypotheses—and she, she had no Swedish legitimization. I did not believe in miracles, not in magic formulas. Neither did I believe in the bureaucratic red tape which had denied her a license which she had earned long ago. I knew she had substituted for a number of doctors in provincial towns. But I didn't worry about this—it was not my business to investigate what I couldn't judge anyway.

I surrendered Anders and myself into her hands. Her examination, as far as I could understand, differed from the others in only one respect: it seemed directed to a goal in a way that was new to me. I hadn't told her anything about Anders' right side. Too many times had I pointed out his spasms and his peculiar way of grabbing objects without being able to hold on to them; I did not wish once more to confront a skepticism I was unable to handle.

This woman doctor—I had a feeling she was Austrian but felt it unimportant to ask—was busy with the physical examination, Anders lying naked before her, his arms and legs in the air. The usual reflexes were tested in the usual ways. Anders followed with great interest all her activities. He stood up and let her feel his muscles. She handed him his little undershirt:

"Put on your shirt," she said.

I quickly stepped to his side, eager to help, to make it go faster.

"No—let him try by himself," she said, warding me off. "I want to see how he does it. We're in no hurry."

Anders kept struggling with his shirt—he had never put it on by himself before. I tried to explain, but she interrupted:

"Let him put on his shirt by himself in the future. He is quite capable, and it saves you time."

"I thought the same with Boel, I tried to teach her constantly, but she never learned."

"This is not Boel, this is Anders," said the doctor, firmly. "No two children are alike. Anders can put on his shirt by himself."

And then I realized this double handicap, this to be forced to repeat the same pattern, which isn't the same, only seems to be. It recalled to me my childhood dream, when I tried to find a path I knew well, and then—in all the fearfulness of a nightmare—the path didn't look at all as I remembered it, nor did it run through grounds I knew. And I would start to run, with ever growing fear, and the path would turn ever more strange, sometimes like the one I remembered, and again different, and soon I would lose all sense of where it might lead.

"That's just the trouble," I said, wearily. "One thinks one knows all. One has certain ideas in one's head—they have been there for many years; one thinks one understands. One cannot imagine it should be different from last time. Even though one knows it might be different."

"But there is nothing alike with these two," said the doctor. She knew about Boel through Ingeborg, the lady with whom Boel had her home. "They are two entirely different children! You must realize that!"

I had said to myself, as well as to others, that no similarity existed. I had reasoned to myself that there could be little likelihood of similarity. Yet, I had acted as if it had been there. Because it is so difficult to rid oneself of this—as *if*.

Again it was pursuing me, this magic "as if." My whole childhood had passed in the shadow of "if not." Father and Mother lived under this—what would have happened "if not." What would it have been like if Father hadn't had his rheumatism, if they had not sold the big estate, if they had not lost their fortune?

If not.

Now I, in my turn, was living "as if." For a time it had been as if Boel had been deaf or had impaired hearing; now it was

178

as if Anders had been Boel, even though deep within me I knew how wrong this "as if" was.

"If not" never leaves the past; it makes no progress, has no future, no hopes. "As if" lives in a future which perhaps never arrives. Both are false and their likeness is that they do not represent the *now*.

I was very tired, sitting there facing this honest woman to whom any pretense or maybe was so foreign. It was difficult for me to report all my mistakes, to admit my obligation to Anders was new and different, because this time I knew so much more, perhaps too much. This business of anticipating, of getting ahead of things as if I knew every detail—wasn't this a fraud? Never to be expiated? How could I have confided this to the foreign woman before me? And how could she have understood, she or anyone?

She now handed blocks of various shapes to Anders. He accepted one block with his right hand, immediately moved it over to his left and began an investigation. The lady doctor handed him again a block, and now he was forced to keep it in his right hand or let go of the one in his left. He lost the right block, dropped it from the palm of his hand. As usual.

She handed him a toy car, drove it before him, observed him. She handed him a teddy bear, it was soft. Anders had always shown a preference for soft objects—pillows, bears, animals, dolls, and back to pillows—anything soft. I recalled now quite clearly Boel's disinterest in all soft things.

The minutes ticked away; she took her time, this doctor. She was not stingy with this precious thing, time. She was most generous with this costly commodity.

Anders kept busy, he was interested. He was with us, not somewhere else, like the child in the glass ball. He was here, present. Now he was inspecting a little tractor, holding it in his left hand.

"He might be left-handed," I said at last, contrary to my conviction and against my will; as a kind of test.

"He is not at all left-handed," said the doctor. "Then it wouldn't be the same problem. He is right-handed, at least his inclination is. For some reason he keeps training his left hand. But that you mustn't allow. He must use his whole right side more. It is too lazy. It is true that one mustn't force left-handed children to use the right one. It's never done any more; it isn't good for them. But it's different with Anders. He must never be allowed to neglect his right side when he so obviously is right-handed by inclination."

"Is it your opinion then, that there is something wrong with his right side?" I said, and felt like a cheat. "In pretended surprise" as the saying goes, although I wasn't at all. I was only waiting, would not put any words in this doctor's mouth, nor give any hints. I didn't pretend, I was only waiting.

"It seems to me he has a marked under-function in his whole right side," said the doctor, and I felt I could hear an echo from my own observations during more than two years. "He is in some way weaker in his right side, whatever the reason might be. It isn't pronounced enough to be noticeable at once, but if you look closely his right side appears to be less developed. I wonder if he might have had some injury to his left cerebral hemisphere—you know, the left side of his brain? Are you familiar with anything of the sort?"

Now at last I told what I knew; I told about my operation, my observations during nursing, of my apprehensions. She listened with a thoughtful wrinkle between her courageous eyes. When I was through she only said, kindly:

"I don't believe things are so very bad with him—he is still so little. There is plenty of time. We have learned something and only one problem remains: we must find out what we can do about it."

Perhaps it was wrong, perhaps it was right. I am not the one to judge, indeed, I ought not judge. I only know one thing: this woman gave me a program which I had longed for. She did not say anything of speech training, nothing about those things I instinctively knew would not find approbation among my "usual" doctors. But she gave me an outline for action, however unpretentious it might be. And action always means motion.

180

Motion, in turn, always means a change. A motion can point forward. This is essential.

I was sufficiently hardened by now not to abandon myself to dreams; perhaps I was even too skeptical. I was not inclined to believe in anything, I was afraid. Afraid to be contaminated with false optimism, and equally afraid to turn from optimism that was justified. Indeed, I was in a dilemma.

This lady doctor told me, however, simple and obvious facts, so simple and obvious that a doctor usually forgets to touch upon them. But she did not forget; she did not hesitate to remind me of them. She was a doctor and teacher at the same time. Humbly, without pretension to exclusiveness, or other imposing extravaganza, she was plain and simple an honest mother speaking to another mother—for one purpose only: to teach elementary but essential facts.

Anders must be kept in excellent shape physically if I were to expect anything from him mentally. So obvious. Any doctor could have told me that. The fact remains that none had. It was too simple. A doctor's words must carry some touch of magic, must lie a little beyond the language the rest of us use in daily talk—otherwise keep silent.

This lady doctor gave such clear and everyday directives as none in the long row of doctors I had sought ever had given me. About diet, exercise, toilet training, sleep, elementary medicinal care, time and habits, bathing, care in general. Instructions which are quite familiar to me, but, perhaps just because of this, never have assumed the importance they should have.

What put her in a class by herself then was neither her keen observations of Anders' functions, nor the optimism of her prognosis. No, it was the cheerful obviousness with which she counted on a plan, a future in which his limitations are not definitely established. She told me something of what I should do and shouldn't. She spoke then of activity, not passivity.

Nor did this doctor mean to give up after she once had given me her diagnostical suppositions and medical-educational advice; she was not—like so many others—a little re-

lieved when the whole thing was over. Instead, she asked to
see Anders again, even made an appointment. She did not
leave me alone with nothing to face the empty months and
years ahead.

Still, I knew as I left her I would not refer to her when I
encountered Authority. I would act the coward. I knew I
would not risk the consideration of my medical friends by
admitting I had sought her. I already felt how they would
belittle her words, crumble her arguments, put her in her
place. No, this I could never confront. This would rob me of
everything.

And no one would put anything in its place. They would
only relegate me outside, in a sort of kindergarten for the
uncritical ones, those easily taken advantage of, the superstitious.

Therefore I would keep silent about this visit. The barriers
are too high; those long ago supposedly buried class differences, once called guild barriers, are still very strong: she
doesn't have a Swedish license!

With summer came promptly a reminder, no longer to be
denied, of my heavy work with Mother's moving: it became
necessary to perform another operation on my leg, rather, a
minor adjustment; a pin must be removed from the joint.
But it was still an irritating reminder that my side step on
the stairs could have consequences which I would not be allowed to forget for the rest of my life. Interfere with my interests on many planes.

I went again to the same hospital. It was a hot early summer,
and Bengt was for the moment in Brussels. The hours in the
hospital assumed a long loneliness without meaning; I could
not escape thinking of the past. And when I returned home
the question marks had not lessened. Yet, there was during
those early summer days an expectancy of new paths to
tread, as yet unknown to me.

Only much, much later would I be able to view the following autumn with regained equanimity. The summer had brought a few enjoyable weeks, family entertainment quickly to be forgotten. Bengt, Lena, and I had gone to a family reunion at Torekov, where it was decided to form a family society, open to all descendants of Captain Junker. It was a cheerful, sunny occasion. We stood in the Torekov church attentively viewing a picture of the Torekov fire of 1737, inscribed "In Deep gratitude for the Lord's saving Grace presented to this Church in Remembrance of the Holocaust by Skipper Eric Junker and his beloved Wife Boel Cresten's Daughter, died 1780, aged 74."

Boel Junker. . . .

At the beginning of the fall term I received a request which frightened and fascinated me at the same time. The State Superintendent of Special Education—the lady with the wonderful laughter—asked me to act as substitute teacher at the Institute for the physically disabled; my class would be the heterogeneous group of hard of hearing children suffering from cerebral palsy, this complicated, double-handicapped group. The task was demanding, I was aware of my shortcomings as an educator—I had never taught a child to read, write, or figure, and here I must be in charge of a class of six children, aged seven to twelve, to instruct them in the Swedish language and perhaps the multiplication table. I would also have to fight for those children's right to education—in my way, I suspected.

There are always so many escapes in the paragraphs; laws and regulations are worded in a manner which excludes the extremes, those who haven't sense enough to keep within the statistical borders; in other words, to keep within that statistical curve which covers practically all human functions. These others, the extremes, are outside the indicated pattern, the strict regulation, the universally accepted. They fall outside the consideration of those busy committee members at the long tables when they make up plans for Society.

Such was the case with my class of deaf and hard of hearing

children with cerebral palsy. That even the hearing nerve might be affected with such a severe brain damage as cerebral palsy—this was a circumstance that had not been included in the paragraphs. No one wanted to acknowledge these little ones, these "outside-statistics"; the authorities could not be expected to have any idea in which group such unexpected lives belonged, or could they?

"We can't take deaf children here, we don't have the facilities." "How could we take the responsibility for children who don't hear and don't talk?" Such arguments confronted me like a bastion at the large Institute for the Disabled. "We don't have personnel to handle them! They should be at the Institute for the Deaf!"

"We have no facilities to handle children with so great a handicap! There are neither elevators nor trained teachers here! Those children would be run over during the first recess, they couldn't manage one day with us! How could we be responsible!" The same bastion at this institute.

But life is not paragraphs, life goes its own way, following different patterns. And so one day at last I found myself sitting in a separate little classroom in the big institute, my incompetence vibrating in every nerve, but my burning love for the deaf child never extinguished through the years. Physical invalidism had been familiar to me since earliest childhood. True enough, cerebral palsy was not rheumatism, but my inborn approach had grown strong through habit. Deafness I had become quite familiar with. But the combination of deafness and CP was to me as foreign as the Chinese language. The teacher whose permanent job it was to instruct these children had my honest and immense admiration.

I met Leif again; he still remembered me and seemed glad —as was I. Again we had our excursions in the car together; sometimes on a Saturday afternoon I might take the whole class and drive some place where we felt completely liberated from the shackles of a large institution, see a little more of the world. We might go to our house at Lidingö, perhaps visit the Scouts, or the airfield, or the zoo.

184

This is now long ago, but one episode has remained in my memory; I have not wanted to forget it.

In my childhood I had known a lady whose seventieth birthday was approaching; I remembered her little home and her valiant fight as a widow with four children. I wanted to renew our contact even though we had seldom seen each other through the years.

It was only natural when we had a moment to ourselves that I should tell her something of what life had brought me since last I had seen her, and soon I was relating something about my heterogeneous class at the Institute for the Disabled.

My experience had been that people would listen to such tales with truly "mixed feelings," but I have made it a habit to speak freely of these matters, because I have a conviction, a cause. I believe that a better understanding lies on that road. In this home, surrounded by so many childhood memories, I felt that my friend from long ago listened with an attention that could mean only one thing.

But the other guests too were now listening, and among them was a lady of rosy hue, a picture of health. She was the mother of a single daughter now married and with a lot of children. "One hen with a single chick, and the chick had suddenly decided to become a hen herself with a whole flock of chicks, . . ." So this grandmother-hen kept cackling.

"Oh, oh, oh, how terrible! Your work must be horrible!"

"Horrible?—It is hard work, but it isn't horrible. It is hard only because I'm not properly equipped for it. Fortunately I'm only substituting, soon they'll have someone much more capable than I."

At this the hen cackled: "Well, I hope they are at least grateful for what you're doing."

I was shocked into silence. When my power of speech returned, I said, slowly: "Who should be grateful?"

"The children, of course! One can only expect that they would be grateful for what is done for them."

"Should they . . . be grateful for the privilege of going to school? Which all other children enjoy?"

"Well, of course, ordinary children have a right to schooling.

185

It wasn't that I meant . . . but these . . . these . . . they ought at least to be grateful. . . ."

I have repeated this episode for one reason: Among my pupils was Ann, and I must linger a moment with Ann because to me she has become the painful symbol of the cruel uncompromisingness of inexorable limitation. And also for the narrow views which decide these limitations.

Ann had cerebral palsy of the athetoid type—that is, she, like Leif, belonged to the "jumping-jack" type. They are the cerebral palsied children whose brain-impairment consists in releasing a stream of uncontrolled motions simultaneously and rapidly when stimulated by the will. As all cerebral palsy-impaired they lack the ability to direct their nerve-impulses. In the old days they were called "spastics," but now this means practically the opposite. Ann's athetosis was very severe.

It also "jumped and jerked" in Ann's brain; she had a remarkable intellectual and emotional vitality. But her place at the Institute was threatened. She loved her school, loved her contact with her comrades. For the time being she was granted the "privilege" of living in her home, to be picked up every day in a special school car. That this was a difficult arrangement I realized fully. I realized also that Ann in this way "indecently" remained outside the norm of proper statistical distribution.

But Ann needed the school she loved so much, and I would not agree to a change that would deny her this. Other solutions had been suggested—perhaps a teacher could be sent to her home now and then. One couldn't do a special favor for one single child—what would happen if all the others demanded the same? There was not enough personnel. Moreover, Ann would probably all her life remain a "wheel-chair-case"; what future could you expect for such a case? And it might instill in the parents a false optimism.

I had not earlier met this "handicap-defeatism" so unabashed. Now at once something appeared to me clearly: I had nothing to lose, being only a substitute, no so-called prestige, nothing. I had only my will to protect this girl's talents

186

against an enforced denial of education; against a denial of companionship so essential to this little girl of definite social talents.

"She has one single life," I said in desperation. "She has one single opportunity for intellectual stimulation. She is what we in our country braggingly call 'of school-duty-age.' What is the 'school-duty' for these outside the statistic norms? Is it a *right* they are forced to relinquish! Because they happen to be so different from the rest. Have they asked our Lord for this favor?"

During my short term as substitute teacher I picked up and drove Ann to her home in my own car. Before I was ready to leave my position I asked for a case conference with the directors of the school about my class; I wanted to talk to the team of teachers, doctors, nurses, attendants. I threw all considerations to the winds; I felt utter disregard for what might be said about me when I demanded—with great insistence and undoubtedly much arrogance—that Ann's right to schooling must be satisfied.

She got it. No more excuses were made.

Her regular teacher—thank heaven he was a man, Ann possessed in full degree a female's adoration of manhood—has since been able to help her develop beyond a point no one had thought possible. I—without the slightest idea how to teach children to count—was able to make her grasp the multiplication table in three days. Her teacher tells me how far she has gone, this girl who never will be able to speak understandably; she is now typing page after page on an electric typewriter, obtained through private donations, in the memory of Folke Bernadotte.

Thus Ann—with the patient aid of her good teacher—has found a way into the outside world that she loves with more compassion than most of us.

Perhaps the only way open to her.

"I cannot for the life of me see that you are especially depressed or desperate!"

The psychiatrist shrugged his shoulders, and I felt quite lost. I sat wrapped in an old coat because again I had a life within me, and under those circumstances suit coats have a tendency to shrink faster than the budget allows. I looked at the pale, chilly face of the psychiatrist. This, then, was one of those to nurse our craggy souls when God hides his face. I felt a doubt which for a moment overshadowed the secret worry and shame I felt.

"I dare not take the risk, don't you understand—lightning has already struck twice in our home. I dare not challenge fate once more. I'm not strong enough to take the risk."

"Why do you get yourself in that condition then? It wouldn't have been necessary at all."

This man could indeed put people in order; his way of handling my pain of humiliation was without doubt a masterpiece.

I had experienced a pride as always before when this had happened to me, perhaps even more pronounced this time. The gathering in Torekov had made me proud of a new branch on the Junker family tree—did I not have a right to be proud?

But my pride had been premature, it had been without any thought of consequences. I had surrendered myself to this wildly primitive desire which has always ruled me: to live in the center of the drama, to play my self-given head role, to be the center in the miracle of a new life.

Now I had been put in place.

I had been thoughtlessly in love with myself. I had forgotten Boel, forgotten Anders, forgotten my three mentally and physically well-formed children for this infinitely self-glorifying wish once again to be participating in a growing life! Again to be productive.

Now matters had been given their right proportions. My substitute-time at the handicap-school had returned to me my common sense. The perspectives had lengthened. Not only had I during this time been confronted with innumerable problems, with so many mothers with guilt-complexes, so much choked longing and suppressed fear. I had also come to realize that I must respect and admit the limitations of my own strength.

188

Lightning never strikes twice in the same house.

Hadn't both I myself and the sad-eyed doctor at the children's hospital once considered this proverb? Lightning never . . . but when it does strike twice, doesn't then the thought seem close at hand that lightning might have found a special liking to one's house?

This thought had found nourishment during my many heavy walks through the halls and corridors of the old handicap-institute. When I thought of it further, I had during the past years seen many examples of this—the lightning's preference for certain houses. Only, I had not wanted to see, had not wanted to admit. . . . I recalled my own father's sister who had lost her two sons, one drowning, the other in ravaging consumption after he already had taken his M.D. degree. My grandmother's brother had experienced the same fate— one son had crashed as a young flier in the army, a second in an accident. And Grandmother herself had lost three of her children.

Who could say that lightning would not again strike our house? Hadn't I challenged fate?

And besides—hadn't I overestimated my strength, and underestimated my children's demands on me?

In my new tribulation I had confided in the remarkable dentist who had become an M.D. to help his deaf son. He had over the years grown to be the kind of friend I went to in such matters. I had followed his advice—that was why I now was sitting in the office of this pale psychiatrist with the cold heart. I had at long last decided that this little new life must not come into being.

Since, I have often wondered over what often is called the irony of fate. I remember my first scientific attempt, the year I had just entered college. It was a study of the abortion question, and I remember so well when I was given the assignment. A young scientist and his father, who together were pursuing this question, had given me an outline for my work. I listened to them, again and again refer to this incomprehensible word —abortion.

189

At that time I had never before heard the word. When we had come to an agreement about my work, I went directly home and looked it up in an encyclopedia. I was seventeen, and my student-cap was new.

This depressingly rainy autumn afternoon in the psychiatrist's chair the word was no longer incomprehensible to me —it became a close reality.

And much else which hitherto had been alien to me was now pulled out and intimately examined in a way I had not been prepared to expect. I had never thought much about how these examinations took place. I had hardly counted on the need of a psychiatrist for a case like mine—at least not to the extent it was now revealed to me. But in this case, too, apparently a statistic existed, outside of which one might happen to land. A statistic in which, in some way, one must find one's place.

For a woman who did not dare or did not wish to bring a new life into the world—regardless of my unkind fate's caprice—only two weaknesses were admissible: physical or mental. There was no other choice. If the necessary physical weakness did not exist, only the psychic remained. There were paragraphs and squares, formulas and columns for everything. Anyone not fitting into a column must blame herself.

How could I claim any form of physical weakness? I, strong and healthy, the mother of five, never in a hospital except for a broken leg? And this fracture could have happened to anyone, even with an iron constitution, though it had turned out to be a very complicated fracture—in some ways.

No, I couldn't claim weakness; nor were any social conditions listed that would fit me.

"Do you really expect me to certify that you have psychic troubles in connection with this?" the psychiatrist asked, with irritation. "You have not the slightest notion what a real psychic depression is!"

I was sitting in the psychiatrist's chair, filled with an immense, hopeless chill. To take an unborn life—who had given us this right? Was I perhaps, after all, a murderess? Obviously

190

I must have committed some crime, otherwise I would hardly have been treated like this?

Apparently this man possessed much morality and omniscient power the way he talked to me. Had I no right to decide about my own body, or what was in it, even though as yet I didn't know if this had life or not? Had I no right to save my strength for those who still might have use for it?

What was my duty? What my right? And what was wrong? My fumbling attempts to discuss these matters with this man, to gain some idea as to the purely ethical principles involved, met with little success from the pale psychiatrist. He had, once and for all, placed me in a certain category, perhaps my worn coat and far from remorseful look had something to do with this; in any case, he was not inclined to participate in evaluations and discussions. Perhaps he was in a hurry, how could I know, but I was—rightly or wrongly—once and for all relegated to a category, a column, where the profligate, the irresponsible ones were gathered—without discrimination.

To foolishly undertake the creation of a new life—because of one's love for another person, and with respect for the frail and fragile in life which one's belonging to that person means, then in bitter afterthought to realize that perhaps it was foolish—such a thoughtlessness must indeed be punished!

"Good Lord, woman!" said the psychiatrist, "you already have five children, and trouble with two—how in all the world could you act so idiotically! And now you ask that I shall consider you mentally depressed! You look to me the most controlled person I ever saw! I can't believe anyone like you might commit suicide!"

Should I have cried then, yelled, exposed the anguish I suffered? Was that the method?

"Is that the question?" I said, slowly. "Must one threaten to commit suicide? Well, well . . . perhaps I could accommodate you."

The psychiatrist shuffled his broad, yellow sheets I never will forget. He shrugged his shoulders again.

"I don't like these cases at all," he said, indignantly.

"Neither do I," I said, softly.

"Are you really at all depressed?" he asked.

"What do you think?"

"Well," he said at last, "if you can prove that you are, then it's all right with me. You should petition to be sterilized—that isn't so difficult to get through. That would be the best."

"Sterilized? But—why?"

"My dear woman," said the psychiatrist, and his patience had now reached a critical limit. "You already have five children—how old are you? Anyway, you're not going to have any more children, are you? There would be no purpose in that? Or do you think so?"

This was something new, something I felt I must get to the bottom of. Here sat a stranger in front of me who already had placed me in a certain column—among the irresponsible—had he now also picked me among the passé? Or what was the chain of thought behind this suggestion?

"I only think it is a most unusual question," I said. "Theoretically it might be possible that I would wish to have more children—even though my husband and I have agreed that it is best not to have any more. In our case, I mean."

"You intend to get another husband then?"

"I hadn't thought of that," I said in surprise. "But now that you point it out . . . I must admit it is something no one knows anything about. In theory it might be possible that I sometime in the future might get married again."

I couldn't stop myself, I had to get to the bottom of this. I had never in my life thought of getting married a second time; in our marriage we had never spoken of divorce. We had had what is called an unusually happy marriage. The question was academic, but it opened such perspectives that I couldn't leave this doctor without further information. He was, after all, Authority.

Then the psychiatrist said, and now he no longer made any attempt to hide either his contempt or his irritation:

"Would you rather have your husband sterilized then?"

What had I done to deserve this? I picked up the yellow forms, my hands trembling. I could think of no answer.

A few years later when Bengt and I were in India I would have occasion to remember this interview more clearly than ever. We were visiting a large governmental hospital in New Delhi. Our host, one of the highest officials of India, had sent us there; Bengt had some trouble with his ear that had to be attended to. I was now waiting for him in an outside office, which from a Swedish point of view resembled the entrance hall to a deserted, crumbling house. Beside me sat the official's secretary who was to help us find our way and bring us back to our host.

We were talking of the population-problem of India, and my guide was giving me an analytical review that was intelligent, even brilliant. Presently he said, quite naturally and without embarrassment: "We have now five children, my wife and I. We cannot have anymore, because of the economic condition of our country. Moreover, we must set a good example. So I have had myself sterilized. We do that here in India, in the educated circles. We realize, both of us, that this is the most practical way, and most beneficial to our country. In the future I cannot put any more children into the world, either with my wife or any other woman. You must admit it is practical?—The woman? No, we don't want to touch a woman in that way, not here in India."

"You can return when you have filled in those applications," said the psychiatrist, shortly. "Can you do it without the social worker's help? Your husband must sign them too, as your guardian."

"Thank you, Doctor," I said, and rose. "I don't need any help to fill them in. I happen to be able to write myself. I can even read. My husband, too."

It might seem unnecessary for me to describe this bitter episode in my life, but I have a definite purpose in so doing. For this concerns all of us, us mothers of the weak, the separate ones. It is something which each one of us might have to face up to. And I wonder if the attitude couldn't be changed toward any patient with such a problem; if one couldn't argue the for and against with a little more understanding. Those horrible yellow forms—perhaps they have another color by now, at least I hope they have a different wording—is it really necessary to go in for this detailed dissection?

Is the woman confirmed? it asked on one line. Blushing in anger I wrote *No!* And at the question Why not? I tried to explain the complicated family situation, our economic ruin, our invalided father, stricken just in those years when I should have attended confirmation classes. Instead I spent my time running to the bank at the last moment, if Father had been able to raise the required cash for some defaulted note.

Has the woman been convicted earlier? was another question, and in a fit of grim humor we both wrote: Only for illegal parking.

What bearing could these questions have on the "crime" that was mine? I never learned.

I had to visit the psychiatrist once more—it was within his domain to recommend or deny my application.

My humiliation this time turned out to be even greater than at the first call—because this time I met an entirely different human being. Was it because he actually had been rushed the first time? Or had I misjudged him?

Because this time the psychiatrist greeted me with great consideration; it was as if, through some invisible magic, I had been transferred from the column of the lewd, to the one of the honorable, stricken with an unjust fate. His respect was immense—in some way he had become enlightened by his colleagues perhaps. I had been given an identity.

The gynecologist was sitting at my bedside—this was not the one with the blond hair and the kind eyes and the big ears. But apparently he had taken on some of the understanding of his colleague, for he looked at me with kind eyes full of comfort offering me something for what I had lost.

"Dear Mrs. Junker," he said. "Don't be sad. One never

194

knows—perhaps it's better this way. Only don't be sad. Try instead to get well and strong as soon as possible. And try to draw a line across all this. We want to help you. We will take care of you as well as we can. By the way, I am inclined to believe that the fetus had no capacity to live, as far as I could see."

I turned to the wall.

XI

The difficult months of studies that followed this dark fall I would rather forget. I had no strength left to help Anders fight his awakening sense of inferiority.

The situation was also new to my experience: Anders knew, not only that he was younger than Riken, not only that the difference in age was natural, he also knew there was a much greater and much more complicated abyss between them. He felt it. And in his way he took revenge for what fate had denied him in equality.

The situation was also entirely different from Boel, the child in the glass ball. I had never noticed any rivalry between Boel and the other children, and I had never felt her suffering any inferiority *vis-à-vis* her brother and sister. Boel had been "happier." Anders was not "happy," at least not in Boel's sense.

As a distraction I placed Riken in a kindergarten, but she

was not pleased to be away from Bengt or me. It was only the following year I became familiar with a fine kindergarten in Stockholm where the Montessori methods were used, when a tactful and wise teacher at this school managed to solve Riken's somewhat shy attitude toward other children and develop her natural desire for contact and stimulate her positive wish for action. Perhaps it was not to be wondered at that Riken ripened prematurely in a most unusual way; she had a quick perception and employed quite early a surprisingly correct terminology; she was mostly surrounded by grownups who talked a great deal on many subjects. Several of her dolls were suffering from brain injuries—cerebral palsy, hearing-defects, myopia.

Anders lacked all the prerequisites to keep up with this speedy development; he learned instead to use his small fists.

I myself was working intensely to climb the last steep steps on the academic ladder to reach my much-too-hurried final examinations; I was cramming, among other reasons, to forget.

The dark months, however, would eventually come to an end, as everything in our lives is a constant change. By and by my great humiliation would bring me this, that a great many things would sink to the bottom and become inconsequentials.

And when the dark months had passed through the winter tunnel—this year blacker than ever it seemed—at last a stream of light dawned at the tunnel opening. The festive day came when my last examination was over, at least for some time, and I could close the door of my study-cell and come out into the open. And now I realized that my forced studies had been my best help in carrying on a life that for a time had seemed too heavy to endure.

I had to shelve for another year my old dream about deaf children's visual perception; the Superintendent for Special Education, the lady with the hearty laughter, had asked me to act as secretary on a committee to speedily examine the conditions of brain-injured deaf children; the time after my examination was to be filled with this problem.

Boel was now in good hands; Anders I pushed onto the future. His speech was greatly delayed, but there was no doubt but that he would be able to talk. He could form simple sentences, like "Annis sleep," "Annis eat," "Annis go car," and I knew I must not force him. Ripening maturity, the natural foundation for the acceptance of language and the use of it, must first make its appearance. This I could not force, be my will ever so great.

The brain-injured deaf children stole days and nights from me. But I myself had made this choice. During endless discussions some members of the committee became my cheerful friends, perhaps all of us realizing the absurdity in attempting to solve an insolvable problem in a short time. Meanwhile the winter thawed away, the spring vanished as quickly as ever, and suddenly it was summer. That summer we bought a small country place out in the archipelago which finally was to conquer completely not only the heart of Bengt but also his youngest son.

Old Farm, or Old North-Wood as we renamed the place, had been a real coast farm in the old days. Wild creeper, roses, and honeysuckle covered the red-washed walls of the house; inside the beams bore witness to much labor of love in the eighteenth century. Through the narrow panes of the living-room windows we could see the shore and the fishing boats and our little smart sailboat anchored in the bay. The pungent seaside air struck me as in the long ago days of childhood. Here we had found this mixture of country verdure and the sea's proximity, yet protected from severe winds so that bees and bumblebees found it a haven in the search for nectar among the multitude of blossoms. Everything was there of what once had been, and yet all was refreshingly new.

We all came to love this place. Yet in moments of nostalgia I sensed a sort of unrequited love. It was a place to evoke dreams—of peace beyond a harassed city life, of new rest. And I knew this peace was not for me, the rest not mine.

I had my "other home" so far away. It was as if a triangle-drama slowly were unrolling before me, the triangle of our Lidingö home, our Old North-Wood home, and the home where Boel was. A hundred-and-twenty-mile triangle, reminding me of another summer when Boel had been at the large institution. And I was being assailed by the same vague feelings of guilt, as perhaps everyone is when interwoven in a real triangle-drama.

Yet that first summer was to be an unforgettable time of joy. We relived not only the mood of our childhood paradise, but we also experienced youth and beauty in an entirely new way: my brother's young daughter who once had spent a few years with us when we were newly married returned to her homeland for a festive visit. She had now blossomed out as a young and accomplished actress on the other side of the Atlantic, and we enjoyed fully the renewed association. She was beautiful and hadn't changed.

Anders was in good hands—we had a new maid of the kind that was spoiling me; Heidi worshiped Anders. That first summer made its impression on him, and he advanced a few steps —forward.

That first summer, then, was active and happy.

The whole autumn was to bring much new forging in the goodwill chain, a lot of activity for the future, which made my latest scar heal so fast that I soon did not discern it; I only knew it had been there.

Little by little I had been caught in the concerted effort to help handicapped children. In a small home for mentally retarded children in a suburb of Stockholm the results were particularly encouraging.

Here I could now look forward to a new mission.

"There exists among developmentally inhibited children and youths one category that is especially neglected as far as education and interest from the Government is concerned. . . ." How many petitions with this introduction didn't our Association write in those days and during the years to follow? Again we were up against the brutal shortcomings of statistics. We were concerned about those "set apart" in real meaning, those who had "fallen off" the many public communication systems and landed at the side of the road as it were. There were a few sentenced to live their own life in idleness and without comrades. Their hope for a future had no counterpart among the majority of the mentally retarded. The group was too small to be given attention at the long conference tables.

"It concerns those children who—during adolescence, and perhaps all through life—have to remain at home, unable to fit into any publicly-sponsored training and education for handicapped," our petition continued. "One can hardly over-emphasize the importance for these children and adolescents to attend for a few hours some day-school under competent instruction. Not only is it valuable for the children to gain knowledge in manual crafts, to experience the joy in creating something beautiful and useful, and learn according to ability to perform daily chores; it is also of inestimable importance to the parents. Partly, to ease the often hard care of the child, partly to offer a harassed mother some comfort, in the feeling that her child, no longer idle, is given an education that might in some way at least correspond to the opportunities offered normal children in her neighborhood, opportunities taken for granted by them."

We wrote, we petitioned for aid from official as well as private sources.

The small day-home and training center was equipped, by willing hands, with kindergarten material, toys and gymnastic equipment, to serve as a temporary day-place for children who had not yet made it apparent whether they belonged in the category of "educable" or "trainable" children, the only two alternatives as yet available. In a way it was an observation class for babies; the older pupils were supplied with looms, kitchen equipment, work-benches, and sewing implements.

All of these children, in a sense, were strays in that no-man's land of inaccessible vocational training, not only because vocational instruction as such often is neglected in an age when we are short of trained instructors, but even—and sometimes entirely—because these youngsters could not assimilate any vocational instruction to talk of. It concerned youths whose in-

200

tellects were not sufficient for the demands of learning a craft, however simple.

"The grave intelligence defect among these pupils demands an individual guidance in every form of occupation we can offer them." This wording explained the whole story of what we tried to do.

The little occupation and training center—like its successors on the same principles—is a monument to the memory of Magnus.

It is the finest tombstone he could have; this boy who lived his fourteen-year life in the shadow of a progressive cerebral defect that eventually robbed him of both sight and mind. It was Magnus' mother who was the driving force behind the day-home idea. She was later for many years to devote her whole energy to our national association, our Swedish NARC.

But Magnus did not live to see this.

Magnus' mother had help from many. When the home opened, new curtains, sewn by mothers, fluttered before the windows; lamp shades and kitchen aprons, towels and pot-holders came from many women's busy hands. This whole little center bore witness to much labor in many bazaars.

Many shared the burden; examples can easily be mentioned. The center would never have opened its doors if it hadn't been for Gunilla's parents. Gunilla's father had influence in community affairs, and he was one of the most important pillars during the first years.

I myself was again carrying living cargo in my car, this time not so silent as during my activities in the "Red Knot." There was Fritz who didn't think a Vanguard was anything to brag about; he wanted a Mercedes—wouldn't be satisfied with anything less. Fritz wanted to explore the universe; he had designed in his own mind a missile for the moon, he insisted, and there would be no complications; one to Venus was only a child's play.

There was Mona who played with her "little ones," cheerful and friendly; there was Eva, a severe spastic; there was one mongoloid Ove who sang, sang, sang—songs and the latest hits—for "Mrs. Junker." There was Tore, and Bengt-Arne with the kind, brown eyes. And again mile was added to mile by my wheels.

Behind our Association's united effort was, last but not least, Jorgen's silent hand—Jorgen who himself never was to see the fruit of this effort. Jorgen's father and Jorgen's mother struggled during long evenings with that numerical *tristesse*, debit and credit—an ungrateful strife with insufficient contributions, shortage of funds, the annoyance of meeting this obligation and delaying that one, the many stipulations and paragraphs that must be obeyed—all this was the duty of Jorgen's father. How many petitions didn't we draft together: "The Authorities, already in 1954 recognized the need for further care of developmentally inhibited. . . . Several years now having elapsed without due attention . . . we are awaiting further. . . ."

There was a certain monotony in this repetition, this never-changing *awaiting further*. Soon we came to a conclusion:

There was no reason why public and private effort couldn't go hand in hand; each needed the other—we could not get along without each other. The personal experience, the individual case, would always lead, show the road, and point out the need. So it has always been, always will be. No public care, however perfect, will ever fill every need, never find all those who have fallen along the roadside. We must help each other—this is life's simple demand. All of us must realize this, and accept it.

Today—when I write this—we have in our community, beside a couple of occupation centers, also a summer home, in which Kristina, another Anders, Torgny, Jorgen, and Goran each have their anonymous share. Each one of them has forged his or her little link in the chain, and none of us worry because all the links look alike.

It makes a chain strong—when all links are equally broad, equally heavy. Such a chain has a strength within itself; it will win out over the skepticism of the long conference tables, at last. It will show that something can be done, with the effort of all for all.

"The danger comes from over-training. I've said it before, and it can't be said too often. You must be patient, wait for the ripening."

Again I heard these words, I don't know how many times he repeated them, my friend the phoniatrist.* I knew he was right, that he knew what he was talking about. I looked at his sandals and the slender hands he kept clasped over his knees. This waiting was hard on my patience.

"But . . . there must be something I ought to do? Something I could start with?"

He looked at me with kind, compassionate eyes.

"One must be very careful—you're too energetic. You must wait. Wait and see," he repeated.

Anders had visited his clinic for an examination, the usual one; cautious observations had been made, and the usual, over-ambitious mamma-attempts to point out the not yet stabilized accomplishments had been tactfully denied by the doctor. I felt a coming-on fatigue, the kind one feels with something unaccomplished. I felt I was caught in a perpetual waiting.

I took Anders' hand in mine, asked him to bow to the doctor, and walked slowly out of his office, out through the long hospital corridor, out to—a continued waiting.

Wait and see. Be careful.

Apparently I was condemned to waiting in inactivity—in all fields. On the inner and the outer plane. Anders on the inner plane. And on the outer?

* A new speciality in Sweden is phoniatry. The phoniatrist is an M.D., originally an otologist, who has developed his speciality and concentrated it on speech impairments not only caused by diseases or defects on ear, nose, and throat, but by brain injuries, etc.

It was not only the many petitions, "... awaiting word from county authorities to execute their plans ..." that had to do with my waiting during the time that now began. Autumn had brought me a new secretaryship. It concerned a much broader field this time—it was a "general review" of the standard at "the different types of institutions which offer care, possibly in combination with education, for those of minority age," so said the governmental directive.

"Concerning these institutions, foremost among them being schools for the blind, the deaf, the epileptics, homes and special schools for mentally retarded, institutions for psychopathic and neurotic children, those crippled, and children's homes, critical complaints have from time to time been raised against the difference in standards between institutions, as well as the care within the same types of institutions. . . ." I read further, and thought for a moment about this formulation.

Was it then, first and foremost, differences they were after? Would everything be well if the institutions were alike—regardless of whether they were run equally well or equally badly? This was an interesting problem. By now I had a great deal of experience with institutions—ultra-modern big institutions, old-fashioned big institutions, modern small homes, half-modern small homes, older small homes, medium large institutions, old and new, private institutions and public ones, care under supervision and without.

The only factor of real importance that had struck me in these many institutions and homes was the atmosphere. And it often seemed that this had no relation either to the size or the age of the project. I felt that the government directive just had happened to take this formulation.

It said also that it would be "desirable at this time to obtain a review of conditions and needs at institutions for children and on this foundation probe the possibilities of a more uniform standard of care."

The line of thought was evident—it was first and foremost *uniformity* that was intended; uniformity at any price?

204

Well, at least uniformity must have a reasonable basis of reference, a purpose—shouldn't it aim up rather than down?

Of course it had improvement as its goal, no question about that. "In principle the institutions ought to operate with the view of offering the greatest possible comfort for the inmates, at the lowest possible cost to the state. Especially concerning the more exposed element of the clientele—the children—it is urged that no excuse may exist to allow some inmates to endure a depressing institutional atmosphere due to delay in support or lack of necessary equipment, while others enjoy the stimulating care and comfort a modern institution offers. Such great differences in standards might have a more marked effect on children, for whom the institute is aimed to substitute the home during the most formative years, than it would have on a mature clientele whose life-situation has had time to stiffen."

Amazing. The "difference" did not wish to leave the directive—it ran like a red thread from beginning to end. How did the individual experience this difference, the individual child? Who only could be at one place at a time, with small chance of knowing what other places were like?

Did they aim to satisfy the demand of specialists for increasing differentiation, or was it that vaguely expressed "uniformity in standard of care" they had in mind? I could make neither head nor tail as to what the question was about. Where was the individual?

Children with different handicaps seem to me to have highly individual personalities—almost in higher degree than other people. I knew from experience how different their demands could be, both in respect to care and surroundings. There were children of a certain type; for example, many of the so-called mongoloid strain, who had an extroverted, social disposition and seemed at their best when in contact with many children. And there were children of Boel's introverted nature who only withdrew further within themselves if they had much company about.

I knew deaf children with a natural contact-hunger, and others who turned frightened and nervous if surrounded with comrades. I had noticed how most of the blind sought contact—but wasn't this because of purely practical need? Mightn't it just as often happen that a blind child would have liked to be alone, if this had been possible?

Moreover, isn't this true with all of us? Some are able to "sleep like logs" surrounded by people, while others can't "close their eyes" if forced to share a room with a single person.

I could therefore not entirely subscribe to this one-line pursuit of uniformity which I read on and between the lines in the directive. To a person who herself has a handicapped child the question of the uniformed standards hardly seems the most important. Obviously the personnel at the institutions for quite natural reasons will consider it rather important, yet seldom as important as we imagine. My personal experience had shown me one thing: to those who have chosen this field the care of the human individual assumes a greater importance than the many material questions so grandly stipulated on paper which we imagine are all-important.

It is hazardous to decide if people, big or small, are happy or not. It should be and must be hazardous. It might be difficult to get normal children to feel happy in a collective group. In the name of justice it must therefore be permitted the handicapped child to feel unhappy, however great "uniformity of standards" is effectuated between the different institutions. And however great the differences one tries to erase.

Who could be sure to feel happy if he were forced to spend all his childhood and adolescent years far away from his home and in surroundings where none of life's most intimate daily happenings were allowed to remain private? How difficult it is for most of our young men to endure with equanimity their life in a military camp. And yet, this is only for a limited time, and all are young people without any physical—and perhaps not often with any psychic—handicap.

Some forms of collectivism might be necessary; no one could deny this. But enforced collectivism, perhaps lasting for life, obviously has great shortcomings and moments of "unhappiness" for the individual. This seems so obvious that one can only be shocked at the storms which from time to time blow up over this question.

Storms are in a way useful, and I don't regret them. On the contrary. What we parents fear more than anything, I believe, is that our children might be forgotten, lost in a flood of paper. In the long run a storm is bound to bring something good in its wake—it carries with it motion. And in most cases this motion is directed *forward*. A change takes place, even though it might blow unpleasantly hard for a while.

It is hard to keep papers lying in a desk basket when the wind blows. But it should not blow hard enough to wreck the building.

To pass the buck between various departments, which often happens during these storms, seems to me like the children's game "the ball burns," and you must quickly pass it to the next fellow. Now he has it, now he must pass it on. Next moment another one has it, and it is his turn to pass it. Such games seem without meaning or goal.

Who is to blame then? Who has been caught with the ball?

The fault is with life in so many cases. Too often. Because life has made us all different, all individuals. Because some of us have been born with one or more handicaps, others apparently with none. Because we react differently to our handicaps. Because undoubtedly we will keep on being different. Lastly, because we are even foolish enough to die at different ages, and in different ways. It is the fault of life that we stubbornly insist on remaining *individuals*. The individual, no one else, is the contending partner in this case. But we do not consider the individual, we consider the group, the statistically controllable.

It should be obvious that from the point of view of the individual the institution is an absurdity. And because of this it is fundamentally unimportant to sit at long conference tables and discuss whether or not children are happy there. How does one go about an inquiry into the abolishment of individuality? How does one inquire into a mother's pain?

207

Or a child's longing for this mother? It is not a question of on which desk or in which basket those papers lie; this concerns people, not paper.

It requires people to take care of people. Human warmth is not in some natural cause-and-effect relationship with the size of funds made available, the standard of furniture, grade of linoleum, or toilet seats. Life does not change because someone has been given a handicap, another one not. Life remains the same. It is always, and foremost, a personal concern. A private concern, perhaps.

I have always believed in individually-directed care of all kinds, for children as well as grown-ups, believed in "the principle of the small group," the small departments, whether in separate small homes, or in small departments in the large institutions. My opinion is in no way original—it is discussed constantly between specialists in the field, in the daily press, in public speeches. Yet, with astonishing inexorability, with stubborn clinging to a rationalism that likes to be fooled, new, big institutions are planned. "It is easier to get help if it is centralized. It's more rational to have a central kitchen. It is also cheaper," are the arguments. And so one builds. Big. The central kitchen idea has passed by the human being in the race.

But there is still no waiting-line of personnel. They don't seem to long for central-kitchens and standardization. Because they too are individuals.

Those vaguely formulated—yet so apparently indicated—attempts to uniformity which colored the entire contents of the royal directive I had received, made me startle, awakened in me an interest which had so strong an effect that I did not hesitate to put aside once more my contemplated studies concerning deaf children's visual perception, that I might be able to devote my time to this investigation. This seemed to me much more important—to act as the secretary for the committee that was now being formed.

I knew that the secretary's role in such a study ought to be that of a laborer—I had the long nights with the deaf, brain-injured children too fresh in memory. And I realized also that

208

the problem of the deaf's visual perception would be pushed into the background. But I longed to work *forward*. I hoped to do something useful. And it was a field that lay intimately close to me—those *other children* occupied its centrum.

That was the way I saw it.

⚜

That fall had brought further signs of development and a forward stride: a new activity was under way in the Scout Movement which promised even more rewarding results than the earlier one. The ground had been well prepared; this time the effort was made hand in hand with the Red Cross, their organization so much larger. They were so many more. Enthusiasm and will to co-operate were the bywords of this action; indeed, it carried the name of the great man who once had been at the head of both these organizations in Sweden. It carried his name in remembrance of the September day, ten years earlier, when he had been killed in Israel. (I still remember that day very clearly, when I had listened to the tragedy over the radio in my bedraggled pension; Boel was still in her mother's life; infinite eons seemed encompassed in the ten years that had passed since then.)

"The Folke-Bernadotte-Action for Children with Cerebral Palsy" was sailing with the wind. I could therefore not help feeling optimistic about the coming winter. It was a hopeful sign that "something had begun to move" in the field to which I intended to devote the remaining part of my life. Both private and official initiatives apparently were on the march forward.

My confidence was great.

⚜

How could I have been foolish enough to expect quick action in our committee to correct what was obviously wrong? Had I been blind to the tactics at the long conference tables, the delays, the procrastinations?

209

A parliamentary inquiry—I should have known something of its mechanism! But no.

I still remember my too apparent shock at our first meeting —we held only three during the time the Riksdag* was in session, during ten long months.

"Thank Heaven, we're in no hurry" were some of the chairman's words of greeting, to which I listened with a palpitating heart.

Weren't we in a hurry? How long, then, was life for these chosen ones who had been given this important task? And how short for those destined to live their few childhood years with a handicap? I hoped the lady chairman had been joking when she said we were in no hurry.

Res Severa Verum Gaudium—I recalled how a few years earlier I had stood contemplating this inscription over the entrance at Leyden University. "Only a difficult task offers true joy," was my attempted translation, and I now wrote it down inside the cover which held together the material I began to gather that fall for our report.

And time passed by. . . .

A few impressions have remained.

The members of the committee were, individually, what one doesn't hesitate to call "good people." Most of them were elected representatives at the Riksdag, all entrusted with many committees. I did seem to feel in them a willingness, readiness, and competence to devote themselves to this far-reaching problem.

But they were more cold-blooded than I, and quite familiar with the mechanism of governmental reports. My own practical experience in this work was from the days when I kept busy with research in building problems, where all had been fired with a spirit of go ahead, not unlike the workmen themselves when you hear them singing, "Hand it up! Hand it up!" At that time we had not hesitated to lose sleep, or work long

* Riksdag corresponds to the Houses of Parliament or Congress.

hours. Consequently, I knew very little about the secret conventions of parliamentary committees.

We started with the blind children. Perhaps it only happened so because the directive had happened to name the blind schools first in the long list of institutions. Anyway, it seemed practical—the blind were without comparison the smallest group of handicapped children. It might be good to "train" on a small group.

A few months passed in an inactivity which I still hadn't become accustomed to. At last we visited the large Institute for the Blind in our city, inspected its school, where I had spent many days during our "Light-Point" campaign and felt at home in a way. In spite of the bare corridors of this nineteenth-century building, it had some of the atmosphere I was looking for everywhere.

We were treated to a fine school lunch, served by blind young girls, as an example of their proficiency in housework. Afterward we sat down in the common-room, and the feeling of warmth remained with me, in spite of the bare walls; it was even increased when I looked out into the hall and saw a blind boy and a blind girl arm in arm. My eyes met those of the director for a moment, pleasantly amused; perhaps both of us remembered how fast those years run away, they're so short and dear.

"Tell me, Doctor," said one of the committee members—I do believe she was a woman—"is blindness hereditary?"

"In some cases, yes—but not as a general rule. Cases with so-called *retrolental fibroplasia*, which we have had quite a few of in recent years, is caused in other ways; usually through an overdose of oxygen in incubator cases."

"But in other cases—can it be inherited?" insisted the committee member.

"Well" the headmaster hesitated with his answer, as if looking for assistance. "In some cases . . . there are certain inclinations. . . ."

"Then I don't understand why you don't sterilize them here?"

I stared in helplessness at the director, my heart banging.

"Sterilize them?" he said, and now his voice no longer sought assistance from anyone; it was calm and sure: "I do not agree with that point of view. The genetic laws are such that deviations can appear in all kinds of connections. In all people. We never know in advance where, or where not. Should we then deny these healthy young people the infinite joy of parenthood? Wouldn't this be cruel? Especially as their children probably will have their sight. Isn't it enough for them that they are blind?"

Truly, I thought, and nodded gratefully to the director; our meddlesomeness is great when it concerns what is good or bad for our neighbor.

In the southern part of our country there is a small school for blind children who have some additional handicap. It had long been over-full. In this case it was easy to "consider actions for the improvement in un-motivated differences"; concerning size, equipment, and renewals.

The director greeted us with an enthusiasm that bespoke hopes he had long nourished: a change, for the better. He showed plans, figures, reports, diagrams, statistics. A labor of many years and with many debates behind it was spread on the director's table. The list of needed improvements at this institution was long; it also had long ago lost its flavor of ultra-modern.

We stopped in the corridor, outside one of the worn little classrooms. We had just passed the prayer room where a mild Christ-picture looked down upon us from its elevation above the altar.

"Tell me, Director—have you any trouble with religion here at your place?" A sudden question from one of the committee members was adding confusion to our discussions of classrooms and other requisites. The director, startled, interrupted his explanations.

"Religion?" he said in surprise. "How? In what way would we have—trouble with it?"

"I mean—is attendance at services compulsory, or how is it arranged?"

212

The director stood for a moment in deep thought, then he said: "The fact is—I've never thought about it. There is a minister who comes here on Sundays and performs the service. Our pupils are invited to attend; we've never told them they must. We only announce when services are to be held. And when we hold service . . . then the pupils come . . . in fact, every one of them . . . unless they're sick in bed, of course. Perhaps they enjoy it," he finished a little lamely, almost as an apology. "It is, after all, a certain interruption of the monotony, don't you think?"

"How about the teachers?"

"The teachers?" The director was still confused. "It is quite clear I have teachers here who believe in God, and some who don't. I have always considered this . . . each one's private business."

I listened to this conversation with silent puzzlement; I wondered where in the directive I had missed this question.

There is a terminal for children who fall along the wayside, those with too many shortcomings to fit into any of the regional institutions. It is the big governmental insane asylum in the southern part of our country.

It housed about a thousand grown inmates, and in one separate wing about sixty children. I knew from old its doctor —he had helped out at a scout camp for handicapped boys— and we had talked at length about our mutual problems. He was a genial soul, reminding me somewhat of Emma that time she had spoken of her "little idiots" in her mild voice.

His calm report about the conditions at this great institution had in it a tired touch of resignation; his replies to our questions came in an almost choked voice, with a patience of kind forgiveness.

Our visit was motivated primarily because the blind who did not fit in at our Stockholm institute, nor at any other home, should—according to the paragraphs—be housed at this place, whether they were, as it was called, "difficult" or not. So the law had prescribed.

Nurses with rattling key bunches led us through innumerable bare, gray rooms. Every door was locked, how could it be otherwise? Little children with no understanding of saving life must be preserved to live. Here we encountered children in straitjackets, as a protection for themselves and from hurting others. It was the first time in my life I had seen children in this situation, with no arm motions possible, biting into their tattered bindings, constrained to live in this narrow space.

One committee member, greatly shaken, asked: "Is this necessary?"

The doctor did not reply, the answer was obvious. He only stroked the head of one of the tied-up boys, gently, with apparent compassion that was far from the paragraphs of the conference tables. The boy made a violent motion of his head, trying to bite the doctor's hand.

There was even a little kindergarten, small as a closet, and the doctor insisted he did not want to give it up.

"It is true that only a couple of our little ones have any pleasure from it or can participate in it, but my feeling is we should have one here in any case. I wish it were three times as big."

In that very moment a cascade of building blocks came flying through the "closet" door, a block-building kicked into ruins.

Someone asked: "Tell me, Doctor—which social group do these children belong to? I mean, can they be classified in any special group?"

The doctor stopped, seemed puzzled: "Social group?" he said, slowly. "We here have given up that business of social groups, long ago. But—if I should try to give an honest answer to that question, I believe most of the childen here belong to group number one."

"But how is that possible?"

The doctor smiled, a little sadly. Then he said, with great patience: "I'll tell you how—perhaps the mothers of these children received a more modern, more expensive delivery care than most; perhaps they insisted that all means available to medical knowledge should be used, to save the child. And the children are paying for their parents' efforts in the most severe brain injuries we have in the field."

I tried to help by telling about American research which showed that the most severely brain-injured children often came from the highest income groups.

A silence ensued, broken by the doctor who said: "One thing I would like to point out—the parents who have their children here with me are very devoted to them. But—life is now once and for all what it is. This they have come to realize."

A few committee members stayed in the south an extra day to inspect the external school classes for special education in Malmö, our largest town in the South. Personally I was pleased with this interest because I knew the man who had started this whole system of open classes, indeed, fought hard in the cause of the handicapped, and I was proud of his success. Now, when he no longer is among us—his wonderful enthusiasm extinguished too early—I remember with especial satisfaction the fact that some members at least were willing to devote a day to his work.

It was worthwhile.

The fact that the class for the education of the partially seeing had been opened this year could well motivate our committee to stay one day more for this inspection. Expensive optical instruments had been purchased to enlarge the distorted little letters of the alphabet and make them readable by the partially seeing youngsters; there was an expensive electric typewriter with giant letters, of American make—illuminations arrangements I knew the Americans were ahead in.

The city's school for children with cerebral palsy was quite extraordinary; in it was practiced the type of teamwork we had fought for and dreamed about during our "Folke-Bernadotte-action." Doctors, physiotherapists, teachers, speechtherapists, parents—all worked enthusiastically together in happy optimism.

The preschool for hard of hearing also had some of the spirit we advocated in our early days of the "Red Knot"—

small, beautiful rooms, auditory training in this warm and near contact between teacher and child, necessary to achieve a good result. The hearing classes too worked in an atmosphere of friendly co-operation, and encountering the superintendent on the stairs I was compelled to inquire: "How do you manage it—have you handpicked every one of your teachers?"

"Indeed I have!" he laughed boisterously. "Each one is handpicked, and I love each and every one!"

I met him only once more before his life came to an end. I recalled the first time we had met, many years before; I had been asked to come to his town and give a lecture before a group of so-called prominent citizens, with various ideals and with or without fat bank books. He had been one of my listeners, and I had noticed him nodding when I emphasized the danger of over-protection for a handicapped child. At the dinner afterward we had immediately become great friends and talked longer than was good for his weak heart about our mutual interests.

Why must the tool be taken from the hand of those who so obviously are fitted to use it? Why are just their voices stilled?

Why?

Spring came at last. With it I felt a new enthusiasm, hoped I could give a push to our slow governmental committee. I was getting fed up with the long winter's inactivity. I was burning with desire to work. A thought had ripened. All the many needs, the acute problems that from time to time had made their appearance in the field of care and teaching of the blind, and which required immediate solution, had awakened this idea.

Couldn't our committee make a partial report, at least show a sign—as I expressed it—that we worked while we sat? An active beginning for the needs of at least one little group?

But this was the busy season in the Riksdag; the other members of our committee were occupied elsewhere. I sat alone in my room. I felt it quite natural to suggest positive measures. During the past year our much-pressed lady chairman had called only three meetings. They had had a small result, I felt. They had not satisfied my desire for action; I was growing ever more restless; I must find new ways, on my own. I must use my short life to some other purpose than just awaiting.

Time and again our meetings had been postponed—for lack of time. But I myself had time to spare. I was well paid for my duties, I had been accustomed to hard work since early childhood. I could not see that time was lacking. It was the empty hours that bothered me.

This was a new experience—to be forced to inactivity. I knew how important my activity, our activity, was; yet I must respect the committee's incomprehensible use of this valuable commodity—time, everflowing, never returning. What couldn't we have done, if only. . . .

If only . . . if not. . . .

The shadow of this "if" plagued my days again, as in my childhood world Mother's and Father's "if not" had run its unproductive course—without a future, without hope, without that development, that push forward that was my life's motivation.

But—the push forward was not for me, something I was soon to learn.

At last the day came which I won't forget.

I had made an outline, a sort of sketch for our discussion, about the conditions within the institutions for the blind and partially seeing children, about resources and debts, about positive situations and negative shortcomings, about conditionary solutions in some cases, about urgent needs in others. We had agreed to a date for meeting—the day after the extra-pension vote. The telephone rang as I was going over my figures.

It was the committee lady chairman.

"We must postpone our meeting—will you please notify the other members?" she said.

"Postpone it? Again?" I said, shocked. "Why?"

"This time for another reason."

"What reason? The debate is over in the Riksdag—you must have time now. I want us to discuss my proposal."

"It isn't a question of time now."

"What then?"

"Well—to tell you the truth—I don't think it's right that a secretary should work like you do. So—fast."

What was that she had said?

Now I was on my guard. The usual tactics of the conference tables stood clear to me. This I had not quite realized before.

I had not wanted to take those words of greeting seriously, that time when she opened our first meeting: "Thank Heaven, we're in no hurry." Now I felt the impact of them. In one year we had held three meetings—yet our work pace had not been slow! It had been normal. And I had had the indecency to try to rush us!

I had hoped to be of some help. Life always seems short to me, I had wanted to give something that seemed worthwhile.

But life was long to those around the conference tables. It was so long that the children I now had in mind might well have passed their short childhood years before the chairman's gavel would make a decision—if ever so unimportant. I noticed my hand on the receiver was beginning to tremble. . . .

Well.

For this, then, had I put in all my strength, for this had I sacrificed my dream about deaf children's visual perception—to serve, plain and simple, as a postponement.

What a discrepancy, what an infinitely abyssmal cleft separates him whose heart and head tremble with vibrating nerves because of an unkind fate—and him, the pale, anonymous one who happens to be chosen by the multitude to supply what the trembling heart needs! Or he who—in a certain salary group—is to determine its secret needs. Still, I felt this cleft could be bridged through reaching to each other hands over this abyss.

There need be no obstacle, for we are all human.

Isn't it perfectly all right for each one of us to feel useful in some one line that he thinks is for the good of all of us? It is as right for him who sits at a conference table as it is for the one who never wants to sit there and never gets near one.

Something must be wrong somewhere; some misunderstanding, that must be righted. Hesitatingly, I said:

"Do you, perhaps, feel . . . that I've worked too independently?"

"Yes. You do a lot by yourself. I'm not at all sure that a committee secretary ought to be so independent."

"But . . . but how could it be otherwise—you sitting in the Riksdag all the time."

"There are telephones. And I don't see why you are in such a hurry. There's plenty of time."

"Members of the Riksdag are not easy to reach by telephone. I don't see how I could do much good unless I worked independently? Has this angle ever occurred to you?"

"I haven't thought much about that. I had better speak to the Minister of Special Social Affairs first. But I haven't got the time just now. This much I can say, however—I don't believe we should rush with a report of this kind. I haven't got the time. You pop up all kinds of suggestions I don't even have time to think over."

"But . . . what should I do then? I must at least do something. I was nominated to do work."

"You know yourself the Minister said we need not hurry."

"But a whole year has gone by! I shelved my scientific work for this. I thought I was supposed to help. All I've done is throw away a whole year!"

"Well, you've been paid for it!"

At this I felt a chill within me, growing to immense proportions.

I had accepted a post because it tempted me to try to do something for those children called the separate ones, those handicapped I had called the weak ones. In spite of all, there are some things you cannot buy—monetary payment is sometimes not sufficient for some work.

I had accepted the position because of the children; perhaps to a certain degree also because of the Minister of Special Social Affairs, my friend of the hearty laughter. And she had expected that perhaps I could do something useful. I had failed her, I had failed the children, I had failed something which perhaps I might call a scientific duty.

I had thoroughly misunderstood my job. Now I had been put in my place.

Slowly I put the receiver back in its crutch. Slowly my useless indignation faded away—into a kind of *horror vacui*. I rose and walked back to the family, suddenly extremely tired. Tired, and slightly unwell.

The fatigue I recognized; it was the old tiredness at the *unaccomplished*.

I didn't quite understand what had happened. I had already learned to like this small group of people, appointed with all the authority of the Riksdag to safeguard the interests of a still larger group of humans who were completely defenseless from lack of physical or mental equipment.

I had been led to believe we might do something of value. At our last meeting the members themselves had suggested more concentrated efforts—at least one meeting a month— and the secretary had been asked to suggest concrete proposals. I had even written this down in the minutes, and now I walked downstairs to my cubicle study where I kept the papers.

I read through the minutes carefully and wondered how it was that I had so completely misunderstood a decision by the committee.

Was I so naïve, such a simpleton?

After having canceled the meeting—"on directive from the Chairman"—I called on my friend, the lady with the wonderful laugh. She was in the hospital, and it bothered me somewhat to disturb her with my problem. But I must report to her that I had failed, that neither she nor any of the other hopefuls could expect anything from me. I had been caught in a commission that I had entirely misunderstood.

I asked her to forgive my failure, as I now wished to be discharged from my position.

"I understand," she said, weakly. "You say your time is too valuable—you have too much you must do. I understand. I feel exactly as you. There are other things; life isn't so long."

I wrote my resignation with a heavy heart; I thanked the Superintendent for the confidence she had shown me in appointing me. And I thought this over—how courageous of her to show another person such confidence; without knowing the "indecent lust for work" this person possessed. I wrote:

"I had understood my commission—in a field that lies close to my heart and which has my undivided interest—to purpose some form of useful result to the state." Then I pointed out how our work was directed, as a beginning, "toward one of the smallest categories in the big, heterogeneous group that institutionalized children represent: no action of any kind has as yet been taken concerning the smallest detail."

The pain I felt in writing this was gradually eased, as I wrote the last sentence: "Under the present circumstances I feel it inconsistent with my conscience to draw a salary from the government for a commission in which I am forced to purposeless passivity."

It was a dubious honor for me a few days later to read an editorial in the largest daily—"The Secretary Who Wants to Work!" I felt the year I had lost in inactivity—the meaning of which I never would understand—represented a much longer period of time—it seemed to me unreplaceable as nothing before had seemed to me.

My suggested outline of discussions for improvements in the small category in the large heterogeneous group would now be placed in the bottom of the basket, this I knew. The little school in southern Sweden must wait still some time—it was, after all, accustomed to this. And yet—I felt the long months with the committee had parted me from many important projects. It had separated me from the really essential in the condition of the defenseless; it had built up a wall of paper. And each paper meant further delay. It was like an automatic mechanism, not to be interfered with.

Such a mechanism has its own force, knows only its own

ways. No one on the outside can change it. The rigidity of a nature-force directs it.

For a while I felt it would be long before I could renew my studies on the deaf children's visual perception—indeed, any scientific thoughts that once had fascinated me.

A sort of lame impotence filled the days that followed.

XII

We went to India that summer.

The International Scout Conference, with more than eighty countries represented, was gathering in New Delhi. For the opening the newest hall in the city had been made available, where Bengt could sit in air-conditioned comfort while I trudged through the humid monsoonal heat to visit institutions of various kinds for handicapped children.

This interval, to a certain degree, brought back my equilibrium after my frustration with the governmental committee.

India was different in every respect. As I look back I realize that everything I had imagined was completely unlike the reality. To speak about India with someone who hasn't been there is almost impossible. Already during the taxi drive from the airport to the hotel I was swamped with so many new impressions that words fail me to describe them.

Yet, I was fascinated, and can't get it out of my mind.

Their problems are so hugely different from ours that comparisons mean nothing. The hordes of children with handicaps of all kinds—how could I begin to analyze, evaluate? When you are told that parents will place a child on the railroad to have a hand or a foot cut off to make it eligible for begging and thus earn its living, how could you attempt to judge, estimate? I am not competent. It is too immense a problem. But it holds my interest.

After a time I surprised myself with a horrible discovery: my reactions had changed. Where was the compassion that would have filled my eyes with tears at home? My ears were suddenly closed to the complaining voices of begging children; I refused to look at a leprous stump of an arm stretched toward me; I turned away from infected eyes, half-blind with oozing pus on which flies feasted. How could I have steeled myself so quickly?

Again some time passed; I began to feel that my Western values elapsed. Who could say that we had found the right solution?

I was talking about female neuroses with a young woman doctor, a mother of three. She had the same calm self-confidence I had met in all the Indian women at the Scout meetings. "We need not run after a man in the same way as you," she said, gently. "It is actually an advantage; it's so much easier this way. I have full confidence that my parents have provided me with the best man I could expect. They have had a much greater experience than I, and they wish the best for me."

"But—wouldn't it be terrible if you fell in love with a man and had to give him up because your parents had chosen someone else?"

"Well, I have never been in love with any other man! Why should I? I have a good husband, and we do the same kind of work—he is a doctor also. And he comes from a good family, as do I. Why shouldn't I be in love with him then?"

All was as obvious as the soft indolence in the Indian woman's motions when she walks through the crowded bazaars, her eyes frank—perhaps with a touch of melancholy —her sari fluttering behind her, her path crowded with noisy children, stately sikhs, holy cows, milch goats, hungry curs, honking bicycle rickshas, yelling hawkers, skeleton-thin, turban-bedecked snake charmers, British-dressed college girls, pajama-clad men about town, sleeping rag-piles, and starved cats.

"There are no unmarried women in our country," she said. "We have, of course, a few widows, but now they can remarry if they can find a man; through advertisement, perhaps. But widows are extremely few, statistically speaking. All other women of my age are married. At least that is one problem we don't have here. Isn't that good!"

"Yes," I replied, with some hesitation; I was not prepared to view this objectively.

"Would you yourself like to be unmarried?" she asked, with a glint in her beautiful, black eyes.

"No!" I said, with assurance. "But I would not like to marry anyone against my will."

"Nor would I!" she laughed. "The difference is only that will is such a flexible notion. Isn't it true—you can will what you must?"

I gave up. It was useless to argue from such divergent points of view. I was not convinced that my opinion might be better than hers.

Nehru himself—a dazzling, fascinating experience. His worn face bore witness to work beyond human endurance. In spite of illness he had insisted at being present at the Scout festivities; as had the Santa Claus-like President who opened his palace for a magnificent garden party, where Scouts and Cubs vied with each other in ingenious display of accomplishments.

The minister of education was willing enough to let me see what institutions existed for deaf, blind, and retarded children in this immense land. At the same time he pointed out —with the same tired look as Nehru's—that he had much

225

greater problems to solve than those of handicapped children. In his country it was, above all, a problem to provide schooling for the healthy youngsters, and he thought he had made a beginning. The gravest problem was illiteracy.

"But we do have schools for the deaf in our country also, of course. Would you like to see the Government School here in the city? We have almost three hundred pupils; one of our best teachers had his training in Manchester—I don't think you could teach him much."

I discerned a certain resignation in his voice; I had a feeling that the care of handicapped children in this country resembled an attempt to empty the ocean with a teaspoon.

When I returned home many of my friends who work in this field, asked me: "Well—how was it in India? Could they teach us anything of interest? Something new?"

I realized that any attempt at characterization would be a failure. Perhaps one might say that the Indians were fifty, a hundred, or a hundred and fifty years behind us, it wouldn't matter how much. In any case, one would fail to catch any of the whole, of the particular. To speak of standards would be doomed before the attempt; in one school for behaviorally disturbed children we visited at Delhi the buildings reminded me of sheds or stalls on a Swedish farm. But the young psychologist who showed us around was acquainted with the most modern American literature on his subject; he was also familiar with everything European, from constricted complexes to anxiety neuroses, and quoted Rohrschach with all the enthusiasm of one newly converted.

And the children—it seemed they might have been picked up by chance anywhere from the streets, stealing a bicycle or a mango fruit from a stand—they were entirely caught in an occupational therapy which was in no way inferior to ours; even though they had to get along with sewing machines from the turn of the century, and lathes and looms of equal age in the crowded space on the earthen floor, they had the same effect as all occupational therapy.

One of the two blind-schools I visited gave me the only example of Indian handicap care which I found utterly depressing. It was animal care, with the nauseating taste of begging in the most flagrant form I was ever confronted with. Obviously I was taken for a rich, eccentric American woman, visiting the school only to be relieved of some of my excess thousand dollar bills. The little boys in their dark stalls on the floor were told that they were entirely dependent on charity; "Those poor blighters, what would they do without me— simply die!" the man in charge expostulated with great satisfaction.

Fortunately the humidity was that day so trying that my ever present Rover-Scout considered it his duty to get me transportation back to my hotel as quickly as possible. The repulsive "headmaster" for the blind school followed me pantingly a long distance, apparently annoyed that the dollar bills did not materialize.

Perhaps I should also say that the children in the school for the deaf spoke so well that I felt obliged to look at their audiograms to find the reason. The curves followed approximately those of my own cubs here at home. The tone of their voices indicated that the audiograms were correct; they were without a doubt what we call totally deaf, those that were given instruction. There were perhaps twenty children to a class, but in the higher age groups the classes were much smaller. Those children spoke so easily and with such good articulation I could not find an explanation for it. I am still trying to figure out how they acquired their clear speech.

The journey to India might seem to lie outside what I am trying to convey in this book. But that is not so. It had its place in the pattern, a definite place. Not only did it restore my self-confidence which had caved in after the committee chairman's telephone call, it also gave perspective I needed to face the future.

Summer and fall brought a new care-problem; this time a cousin of my own age had to shoulder the burden. My mother's sister Eva had definitely thrown off the ropes of our earthly existence; she was now living in a senile dementia which had made her kind toward all of us but exposed her to certain risks. Of her brothers and sisters, my mother was the only one living in Sweden, but Mother was incapable of finding a place for her or facing other problems—her old hands were too tired and worn. And Aunt Eva had suddenly and unexpectedly taken to wandering. Thus we had a new nomad among us, albeit different from the difficult one we had housed at the Sörmland lake.

Senile dementia. This too is an abnormality of the mind worthy of consideration; one day when I would least expect it it might hit me. The helplessness is equal to Boel's.

When do our concerns come to an end? When can we count the healthy in the dominating column? I remember that time, so long ago, when I stayed at the fallen down pension at the old estate, the summer I was expecting Boel. I have often since thought of the statistical distribution among the guests.

I remember the retired colonel, with his bib and his hostile shadows. The so-called survival-fittest perhaps do not in the final analysis make up the majority among us, even though we wish to think so when we sit down at conference tables and make decisions for the weak as if they were the few. At the pension that time there was also a paranoiac, one senile, and the Inconvenient One. Three out of eight guests. The percentage is staggering. Shouldn't we look a little closer into this?

In our own daily existence we count with senile dementia as little as breaking a leg or an arm, yet it is most common.

Aunt Eva was sitting in her chair, smiling, and I asked what she might wish for her birthday. She would like ". . . well, to tell the truth, I think I should like a small ring. A little ring for my finger." She looked away with her kind, tired eyes, then picked up a paper I had brought and tried to spell words.

She was an old schoolteacher sitting there, her proficiency in spelling was not yet wholly lost. She put together a few words, then again she looked up, smiling. Not there, yet there.

The senile smile. She was paying her price for a life-long high blood pressure.

"Is Bengt—is Bengt out riding?" she asked presently, and now she was beyond rings and jewelry. "Did he borrow Hazard?"

She was in the land of her youth now; the horse she was talking about had belonged to my father as a boy at their Sörmland estate; she was mixing up Bengt with my uncle Carl; they were identical in the world that now was hers.

"How is Carl today?" was the next question, and I omitted telling her that Carl has been dead since 1947. "Did he go riding on Hazard? They should be back for breakfast soon."

This I could not make clear to Mother; it would have been harder than it once was to talk with Father about Boel.

Mother, nine years older than Aunt Eva, could not comprehend this change; in her brain there was not a sign of ravaging age; I could talk with her as with a woman my own age, aside from her hearing which was diminishing in later years. Her sharp thoughts did not divulge her seventy-nine years.

"Nonsense," she said. "How could Eva be senile—she is nine years younger than I! Do I act senile?"

"Of course not, Mother. But Aunt Eva is. You must realize, Mother, that she is sick," I said guardedly. "She is indeed very sick. Senile dementia is a very severe illness."

We had suddenly been confronted with the problem of finding a place for an old person with senile dementia and with limited means. Again I had to sit down and consider what life brought those who might fall along the wayside.

If an old person becomes a "care-case," if it can be proved that she is unable to manage by herself, then her relatives must make sure that she is physically ill, otherwise they will have to stand in the long line of applicants to a public institution. If her sickness is physical, and if the relatives are able to find room for her in a private home, then public assistance can be obtained to supplement her folk-pension.

Thus, if the senility is in the legs, the heart, or any other part of the body except the head, then there is no worry about being taken care of, even if the only available place should be an expensive private home. Conversely, if the head is affected, the relatives must get together and raise money for the support, or search diligently for some chronic disease justifying invalidism.

I had never thought much about this problem until we had found a private home for Aunt Eva, where she stayed until her death; in the room next to hers there was another case of senile dementia. The relatives of this lady met the obligations themselves, with great effort, because in their case the patient had no other sickness than "hardening of the brain."

Fortunately, Aunt Eva had been granted a number of bodily ailments—high blood-pressure, palpitating heart, cataracts. Her care never became a burden to the relatives.

The first ring I bought for Aunt Eva was too large; the second one was a little girl's ring, too small. By the time I had exchanged for a third ring, Aunt Eva was dead. Christmas had come and gone, we were a bit along in the new year.

❧

A little hand in mine.

I could do nothing with that hand, I had begun to realize my limitations.

"You mustn't overtrain him!" the phoniatrician kept reminding me. "You mustn't give up!" the lady doctor without a license insisted. And my worries grew with Anders' annoyance at his inferiority, his impatience with a family unable to understand his lingo, especially sister's patronizing maturity and devastating charm.

"One must not only think of oneself," said Riken, wisely, when I fetched her from the Montessorian kindergarten. "One must also have self-discipline and education, you understand. Consideration is rather difficult. A man and his wife and a child—that's not an easy situation. You see, one must think of the others first. Like me—I must think first of you and Father before I think of myself. And you—you must think of Father and us. But Anders—he doesn't think at all."

And the little hand I held turned into a fist—Anders' only defense against this wisdom, this six-year-old's philosophy he couldn't reach with his limited functions.

I decided to see my friend from Boel's days, the psychologist. He had already had something to do with Anders' problem, now we discussed it again; it had become too much for me to handle.

The psychologist tested again.

This friend of mine had seen much—children coming and going through that swinging door I once had forgotten to lock. He had no prejudices about accepted or not-accepted forms of treatment, about doctors having a license or not.

"I don't think you can manage this by yourself," he said. "You should let someone else try, because you demand too much. In spite of your better contact with him I feel you should let some outsider try. I'm quite optimistic in this case —he has so many quite normal functions, some even above the average. But he has that difficult profile—his intelligence profile is uneven. There is no co-operation between the different functions when they lie on so uneven a base. The cogs do not fit into each other."

At last I decided to drive down and talk to dear Ingeborg, with whom Boel was staying. She did not have a school to offer, but she had a home; and Anders could go to a suitable special school in the vicinity, like any other boy his age. He would have a home to return to in the afternoon, and a sister. Ingeborg was growing tired by now; she had only three children, but her face lit up at the thought of having someone of Anders' type.

A child who could speak, even though poorly. She had not had one like that for many years. "A child with possibilities," she said, without knowing the happiness she gave me with those words.

The psychologist thought it was an excellent idea.

Then I went to see the phoniatrist. "I can't stand it," I said. "I can't help correcting him when I know he can repeat after me."

"You must wait, you mustn't overtrain him. He must mature." The phoniatrist had not changed his opinion. But he too thought it was the right thing to do.

And so I went to see the friend from our youth, the children's doctor who now was in charge of the big, modern pediatric hospital out on the southern cliffs of the city with its calming view from the windows over the glittering water between the tall, steep, pine-clad shores.

The doctor with the big warm heart and the good cheering words listened and advised. We talked and talked—there seemed to be so much to discuss this time, for and against; questions I myself had struggled with, so many perspectives, so many dimensions.

The children's doctor signed our application papers.

It had become my duty to arrange my aunt's funeral. Among all our Scout friends was also an undertaker, a little different from the usual type; he did not display the sentimentality his profession puts on at these occasions. He seemed the natural one to turn to.

Mother was petrified: her youngest sister was gone, so unexpectedly before her. To the rest of us it didn't seem unexpected. When I spoke to her about the funeral arrangements, she only said: "Thank you, Karin. You've handled it so nicely you might as well arrange mine the same way when the time comes."

It relieved me of much which at that time none of us knew.

I had started to observe at the clinic with my friend the phoniatrist. I wanted to learn as much as I could; I also wanted to forget my inability on the personal plane by trying other planes.

232

All the little patients referred to me taught me something. They widened my view about the Word—so mocking, elusive, yet ever fascinating. I learned to consider—even esteem—this delicate mechanism, this fine, sensitive instrument which speech and language is. More than ever before.

Among the small patients were also those tragically crippled older people called aphasics. I had previously a few times come across this form of speech defect, seen the energetic fight to regain the ability to speak which is the aphasic's fate. A battle with many defeats. I can still hear their embarrassed laughter when they used a word with completely wrong meaning for some object and realized their mistake.

"Cycle," said a thin, energetic man, looking at the phoniatrist's speech therapist sitting at her table, patiently, calmly, even humorously, hour after hour helping children, youths, grown-ups, old people struggle with this enemy of theirs—the Word.

"Cycle," he said, his eyes pleading for some encouragement.

But the speech therapist—the logopede—had been pointing at a fork. Therefore she did not say anything, only smiled, a friendly smile, and pointed to the next picture, a hat.

"And what might this be?" she asked with infinite patience.

"A clock," said the aphasic. "No . . . really, it is actually a clock."

His embarrassed laughter could not change the fact.

And so fate willed it that my observation work with the phoniatrist had as one result that Mother did not have to face the great darkness alone, which she always had feared. This fear had been apparent every time I took a trip; at every farewell there had been a secret fear in her eyes—what if it happens while you are gone? Our journey to India had been her great dread.

We might never see each other again.

Mother had been stubborn; the way old people are. She wanted to tell her "little sister" a last goodbye before the funeral, wanted to offer a flower to the only one of her family

233

this side the Atlantic. In the car coming back from church I had barely had time to tell her that our good friend, the director for the deaf, suddenly had left us forever that morning. I tried to find a comfort in this—think, Mother, Eva had long been sick . . . one must admit she was finished with life. But this was much worse—a man in his best years, in the midst of his work among the deaf children. . . .

"My dear," said Mother quietly. "What will you do now? Whom can you find to replace him?"

"None, Mother," I said, choking. "There's no one like him . . . in the same way. . . ."

I just happened to call her on the phone a quarter of an hour after I had driven her home; a few small patients were waiting for me at the phoniatrist's.

This day Riken had not wished to accompany me to the clinic, as she usually did, even when it was not at all convenient; today I would have liked her to be with me.

But she hadn't wanted to come.

She had wanted to go to Grandmother instead.

"But Grandmother is expecting our cousins for coffee; we have been at church with Aunt Eva, perhaps Grandmother is tired," I protested.

"If I want to go to my grandmother, why can't I go?"

It just so happened. As so much else.

When I called Mother—it couldn't have been more than twenty minutes after I had left her—I realized what had happened. I could hear it in her voice. There was no pretense, no complaint that I had left her, that I always was busy.

It was something else.

Her voice reached me through the wire, alien, distorted from a sudden pain whose meaning she never learned.

We managed to find a room for Mother in the same private home where Aunt Eva had died a few days before—perhaps her bed still was empty.

Mother's brain hemorrhage was a short, blistering hurricane —it was a typhoon that broke and tore down everything in

234

its path, before anyone realized its fury. After the storm came a great calm.

I sat two days with Mother's hand in mine. She was in a deep coma, but at times I could feel her pressure against my hand; perhaps she felt, through her deep veil, that her little daughter was close by—as in olden days. As before. Without the troubles of intervening years, without misunderstandings, jealousy, loneliness. Without the walls of insoluble questions.

We held each other's hands until the peaceful end came. Then I rose, went to the head of her bed and read Our Father.

I had not known about the tenderness one feels when just leaving a deathbed. Now I felt it almost physically. I have never experienced anything similar, except when one of my newborn children has been placed at my side for the first time, and when I have felt it in my love, the great one; the one that rules every thought, every daily doing. Now I felt the same tenderness again, in every joint, in every fingertip. It is painful and blissful, inside and out.

I had not known before that closeness to death—when it is intimate, real, experienced when escorting a beloved one across the border and knowing what happens is for the best— I had not known it would bring me this. A sort of all-love, a smarting tenderness for every living thing. It was almost ridiculous—I sat at the wheel in my car and saw the roughneck with his pulled-down hat try to cross before me. I felt sorry for the roughneck, I willingly gave up my right; after all, it isn't so important. Not nearly as important as one thinks.

I have retained my tenderness.

I cherish it as a great valuable I might lose. As an East Indian bowl, an antique that can not be replaced or restored if broken. I handle it gingerly, cautiously. But there is no fear in my caution. I have no fear any longer.

I was sitting with my hands on the wheel, driving about planlessly in this strange, separate privacy, this moving home that my car had become, with or without my will. It was five hours since Mother had died; for five hours I had been motherless—the last link broken with that generation which was before me. Now I myself was the old generation.

Poor woman back there, hurrying so for the streetcar. You'll get to it. You'll have time. You needn't run. You see, Mother died peacefully five hours ago. She had been panting and fighting for two and a half days. Then she began breathing slower, slower. Peacefully, peacefully. I hardly knew when she took that final breath.

One doesn't know exactly when. Not quite. It is an imperceptible transition, and one remains warm so long after the last breath that a person sitting at the bedside might wonder, again and again, if there won't be one more breath. Nothing one has heard or read about death being unesthetic has held true. Mother's death was beautiful. No open mouth, no rattling. No, instead, like a final gesture she closed her mouth after her last breath. Was it really the last one? She looked as if smiling—gentle, soft. As if all was well with her. As it had been of old. As she had hoped it would be.

And now afterwards I understand what it was, above all, that forced me to her side, kept me there, unable to leave. I wanted to protect her, as it were, against the scrutiny of others. Isn't just this love? In the critical moment to try to protect the loved one, guard that which belongs to the intimate circle, the home.

This very thing is also important with our children, those other ones. We want to protect them against a scrutinizing curiosity which can destroy. We don't want to expose them without this protection of love. We don't want them to be left to other people without this guarantee.

I feel sorry for you who are in such a hurry. You see—it is so simple, the whole thing, so infinitely simple. You need not rush. These are our conditions, nothing more. Only, we must in time consider them and realize our position. It isn't so important then to catch up with the streetcar.

Not at all important.

After Mother's funeral I seemed to have a harder time than ever. I had so lately lost two people who were close to me, each in her or his way: Mother and Anders. The parting from Mother was in accordance with life's natural course; deepest within me I must have been prepared.

But everything afterward wore on my strength, the whole devastating procedure of handling an old, worn home, filled with memories—bitter, beautiful, sad—yet seldom so happy as life can be sometimes. For each object, old or new, valuable or valueless, decisions must be made, disposals effectuated.

I was tired of decisions.

I had parted from two dear relations in two different ways. I would not acknowledge that Anders had gone out of my life —this I will never admit. Yet I noticed how our family by and by slid into a new conditional "as if," as logically as the truth in the old saw: Out of sight, out of mind.

Anders no longer was included in our plans to the same extent as before now that we did not see him. One cannot expect plans to be made as if a person always was at home, when in fact he was home only at holidays or vacations.

He was transformed into a little guest who came to visit, and I could do nothing about it. He was a dear guest; but a guest.

There were periods after these happenings when life was dark, dusty, shut up in what to me seemed meaningless dead matter. I felt I was digging in hopeless old dust when I tried to dispose of all the ancient junk Mother had left behind; I was buried in a heavy depression of fighting objects. Duties stole my time, made me lose sight of Anders, gnawed on my will to live.

I was tired.

It might happen, in a hypochondriac pursuit, that I tried to blame my utter fatigue on some ridiculous bodily shortcoming —anemia, joint-ache, heart trouble at night.

It was a devastating time.

But that time too would come to an end, at last.

Now I know the remedy for fatigue and utter indolence; there is only one: to go forward, to continue going forward.

The motion *forward*; that is the answer.

We who are the parents of the weak ones have burdens which are common to all of us: we will never be finished like others.

At first our children are small; we wait for the diagnosis to be completed. But—are we ever finished with anything? No. Perhaps we've just started. Perhaps we do get finished with one thing—acceptance.

The children will grow; their type of care or education might be such that we are given a breathing spell. We harbor for a short time the fallacious illusion that we have reached something, a sort of goal. We might call this "placing."

But we will find the goal a false one; first now the problems begin, the real ones that fill the nights with waking hours. What will become of this our child when it is no longer a child, when it is a youth, when other youths go to work or college? What will our child do then? Our child who has grown up?

And what will happen when we are gone?

That is why we are tired. I recognize the fatigue that comes from not having accomplished, not having finished. It is self-evident and natural, it will always remain with us. There is no use in denying this.

However, we can fight it.

If we in indolent laziness accept it, then we might as well sit down at the roadside, throw away our weapons, and suck on a blade of grass, refusing to go on.

I wish to be on my feet as long as I can. The roadside, that tempting rest of indolence is not for me. Not yet.

As long as I am able—on my feet. With the means at my command. They are my remaining, my only, weapons.

"We have attempted to utilize our training center for a certain educational experiment which the county government might wish to take advantage of for its own institutional care. . . ."

238

Our little day-home for training and occupational therapy was being inspected by the county psychiatrist, and the young lady in charge was reading to him our aims and activities:

"Thus we have employed rhythmic gymnastics at regular hours of the week. Modern medical science agrees that rhythm and motion-therapy are important in attempting to develop retarded traits; especially in mental cases suffering from disturbance in balance and motor-functions.

"We have also added a school kitchen that has found great favor with the pupils as well as the mothers.

"It has also seemed essential to retain a few hours' instruction in reading, writing, and arithmetic, as far as the pupils have been able to build further on knowledge gained in other special schools. Even though very elementary we consider it important that our pupils can write their names and addresses correctly, know the value of coins, bills, etc., learn to tell the time by the clock, know the date, the month, realize the change of the seasons, some simple geographic facts and social customs. Our expectations in this field were not very high, but the individual results indicate, to our fullest satisfaction, that our effort has been worthwhile."

I got to thinking about this strong, calm young woman as we sat there in the day-home's little office—a room so small it surely must have been planned for a closet when the house was built.

During the years we had seen this woman at the helm she had developed in a way we had not dared hope. We parents, eager to get going, had perhaps not even contemplated whether our attempts would succeed or not.

And now, confronted with the county doctor, she read her report with utmost competence, smiled sometimes, skeptically perhaps, as she had done when I presented my ambitious plans. Suddenly it struck me, with such force that I felt my cheeks were pale now and my eyes tired:

These are the ones to carry on. Such is the chain reaction of good will. We others perhaps manage to indicate the road a little at times. But the important, the enduring, is done by these who work without fanfare during long days. The heavy,

239

perhaps sad, work is theirs. The monotony of the gray days is theirs. They are the ones to support our faith in our mutual journey through disappointments and difficulties. They are the ones to endure the long, hard drudgery.

And so again I looked into her eyes with their ever-lurking humor. I could build my security and comfort for the future in that look; in her as in her cooperators at the day-home: the therapist, the widow of the director for the deaf, the gym instructor, the kindergarten teacher—all would give me something of this blessed security and comfort that I today saw in this young woman's eyes. We had a fine group of helpers, I felt.

I have heard thoughtless people clothe us—we of this fate—in some sort of hero-mantle. Much is talked about in our circles of sin and punishment. There are those who never cease to look for reasons in the past. But is it then a punishment to have been given this fate? Doesn't it also give us something in return, something that weighs heavily, and lessens the smart of the punishment? Have we reason to clothe ourselves in the mail and helmet of the hero?

We need hardly change clothes, not with the heroes.

It is *the others*, those who keep the spark alive through the many hours, who should be called heroes, at least occasionally. For is it not much more heroic to keep alive an enthusiasm that is not inspired by personal motives?

I am thinking of all those who during recent years have given their lives for our cause. The director of the school for the deaf, the enthusiast down in the south, the great surgeon and specialist in ortopedics whose heart burned for the handicapped, and many, many others. In truth—who is the hero among us?

Presently I turned to the inspecting doctor: "Don't you frighten her now!" I said. "She is the one at the helm of our ship—don't you dare frighten our Captain!"

We moved through the rooms, from the sitting room to the spacious kitchen, this inspector and his assistant. But

240

there was nothing to fear from this doctor. His wise eyes smiled at me, and hope cheered me as he said:

"How could I possibly frighten her—there is nothing here to frighten her with!"

Well, we could sail on. . . .

❧

"History is being written in Swedish deaf-instruction these days; today six deaf youths are graduating from high school in the Blockhusudden School for the Deaf, run by the Swedish Scout Movement. This is the first time in our land that a whole group of deaf youths has had the opportunity to graduate as other youngsters."

I was listening to the voice over the car radio as I drove through the verdant countryside towards Stockholm. A feeling of gratitude swept over me that Providence had granted me moments like this. How many people would stop to contemplate that the announcement over the radio was a victory over the Word that was not in the Beginning?

I was on my way to Blockhusudden. I had asked to accompany me the widow of my friend the director, who had given his life to help the deaf reconquer the word. She was now patiently guiding the trainable pupils at our day-home through the intricacies of cooking. I wanted her help in celebrating this day which her husband had looked forward to.

Her eyes filled with tears when I asked her. No, this she would not be able to do. But the next moment I caught her joking with Mona and Gunilla and hurried them to finish the dishes. Life, in spite of all, must go on. Strong, undeviating, she would remain at her post.

Sun-glitter streamed down over our school on Blockhusudden which now houses three classes. The flag waved in the breeze, parents and friends with flowers in their hands and tears in their eyes, journalists with cameras, TV technicians, officials from the Scout Organization, friends from our "Red Knot" days, all were here.

The festival today was still our own, in a way; this year

for the last time. With the next semester the school would be transferred to the state, a natural development we all had wished and all were pleased with. A development we felt proud of. Our efforts had opened the road, now the strong machinery, the greater resources, would keep the road open, meet emergencies which might have been too much for us. We were proud and pleased, in spite of some nostalgia at the imminent transfer.

Only a few days earlier my Akela friend and I had made our private farewell to the school. We had had a sort of commencement out there with our Cub-boys from the school for the deaf whom we were quite attached to after the years of work with them. As I watched the attractive class I wondered if any one among them would have the stamina to endure a course at the Blockhusudden school, which would open a richer and fuller life. Surely, some of them.

When the festivities were over at Blockhusudden all the pupils had only one thought in mind: they wanted to take a trip to the grave of the director of the Deaf Institute, their first inspiration; they now wanted to pay homage to him.

We piled into the cars and the school bus and started for the cemetery. As we entered the gates the mild sun hid behind clouds, and the first heavy drops fell against my windshield. While the blessed spring rain watered the dust, bringing promise of new growth, two of the students planted a rose tree at the foot of the severe tombstone.

I turned to the girls and said, with some emotion:

"What a pity he isn't with us today. Too bad he never lived to see this day—he would have been so pleased."

The girls had followed my facial motions with great intent to read what I was saying. One of them replied, her toneless, difficult nasal sounds trembling out over the grass-clad graves:

"Yet he is with us."

The girls' eyes were glazed, the boys' looks serious. A deep sense of gratitude filled me that I had been granted this moment. At last I felt some of that victory over the injustice of speechlessness—how many times hadn't I looked for it in

242

vain—an awareness of the tremendous depth of our emotional life, so strong that nuances are obliterated between those who hear and the deaf ones.

According to my custom during these days I turned on my car radio whenever I transported silent cargo, and now Chopin's "Ballade in G Minor" came to my ears. I felt it fitting in leaving the rolling hills of the cemetery. I recalled my own struggles at the piano with the first phrase when I was a child. These friends of mine, the deaf, can never enjoy its nostalgic melody. But their actions today had shown that this fragment of Chopin would have suited them could they have heard it.

But not a depressing, final, fateful minor I felt. Rather, a minor with the future's gushing strength.

A minor in major.

Still one more joint effort bringing joy is a home for summer play now being built by many tender hands. Kristina and Anders (another Anders than our son) are building for others not equally fortunate. They too are handicapped, but are still living with their parents, go to school, enjoy summer, as do all of us.

Anders and Kristina know nothing of their lot in life. In a corner of the world, north of the city, they work diligently, without publicity, joined by others. This summer home will have a lake, a beach, a forest with pines and birches, a flagpole, wooden steps that squeak under summer-warm children's feet, home-woven rugs, fluttering cotton curtains, a leaking rowboat with heavy oars, wasps' nests in the woodshed, busy ants tracking along forest paths to their giant hill, milk and cake in the afternoons, or perhaps soft drinks—all this unmistakably right which all others enjoy.

This home which Anders and Kristina are building offers all this.

Indeed, something to feel happy about.

"Sing, Mummy! Annis vely sick."

Anders had a high fever, his voice almost inaudible; he was

very ill, and he wanted me to sing for him. He looked at me reproachfully, pleadingly. I offered him a piece of candy.

"Mother's little Olle walking through the woods . . ."

"Please, Mummy, not that song."

I held his little hand in mine; it was burning hot.

"Mother's little Anders walking through the woods . . ."

"No, Mummy, not lill'e Annis, 'nother song."

"Shall I sing about our North-Wood home?"

"Please, Mummy, sing Noll-Wood."

I began to improvise: "We're walking to the lake, in the hot sunshine, we're going to fish, with Father in the boat. And the boat is tip-tops, on the waves so blue, with Anders steering. Tuff-tuff says the boat, steer me round the point, out on the blue sea, where many fish we get—a pike and a codfish and an eel and a flounder . . ."

Presently he started to cry.

A quiet weeping. Quiet but deep.

". . . they're hard to pull, hard to pull. . . ." My singing died down.

"Soon we'll go to North-Wood, Anders. . . ."

"Mummy stay, Annis get well. Mummy sleep in Bolla's room, then Annis get well. Mummy stay. . . . "

"Yes, Anders, I'll sleep in Bolla's room. Until you get well."

When I sneaked out through the door he started to whine again, but his voice was so hoarse I couldn't hear it for long.

I stole down the steps, my guilty conscience with me. We whispered downstairs, Ingeborg and I, forging the usual excuses.

She was in his room with him when I closed the front door behind me.

This I can never get rid of. The pain will not leave me, never, even though I keep busy constantly. I will carry it with me, summer and winter, forever.

Yet I do know we have done the right thing with Anders. His development has shown it only too clearly. The cord between us grows stronger with the regular succession of term

244

and vacation, between Järna and home. His word-supply has increased, his adjustment is better.

Driving homewards I castigate myself: admit it, these things are handled better by an Ingeborg, a Granny Kalle, a Mother Atti, a Nurse Naemi. Only, I must acknowledge it. My own plans are so fine, my air castles so tall, but they crumble at the first gust of wind. I am unable to co-ordinate this in the right way—the family and Anders; Boel and the family; Anders, the family, and Boel. Something gets out of line, I'm not able to correct it. Always something. Always.

This solution has proved to be happily progressive. So far. Why do I then suffer from this double anxiety? No one can tell me what is best. I can only see what is happening. I can only help according to my ability; be at hand when needed. And wait. Continue to wait.

Soon I will be bringing him home to enjoy summer—with a new anxiety: he will be at my heels, follow me everywhere, and at last I will succumb.

I know it, the compromises will begin again. Again and again.

And my wish must each time be that he will develop a little more down there with Ingeborg, gain a little more stamina.

The final day, so sweet in childhood memory of summer vacations, the last day was upon us. The long summer was over. A new period was to begin. And again I was assailed by the question, the one that never gives me peace.

Every day this last week I had caught myself searching my conscience, persistently, waking up at night asking myself: Were we doing the right thing?

What is right? Who can judge? Who knows?

For the last time this summer I walked the steep hill down to the sea where his last year's homemade freighter was still floating in the reeds, the nail-mast rusty and crooked, the tackle flagging.

His hand in mine. As always.

"Annis' boat! Annis play boat morrow."

"Yes, Anders, your boat," I answered mechanically.

"Annis play boat morrow."

Silence.

"Annis play boat morrow."

"We won't be here tomorrow, Anders."

"Annis play boat now."

"We . . . we must leave now, Anders." I try to be as gentle as possible, not tell him right out. I trust and hope he won't notice. Not notice the complete change in store.

"Annis play boat morrow. Mummy too play morrow."

"We might not be here tomorrow. First we must sleep."

"Mummy sleep with Annis. Mummy sleep Annis."

"No, Mother can't sleep with Anders now."

It is sometimes called an ice-hand. An ice-hand over the heart. Not a bad expression. From up the hill we could hear the faint clang of our dinner bell, a sound awakening nostalgic remembrances of summers gone by; bare feet over the graveled yard, a border of pungent marigolds framing it; the summer-delicacy of *filbunke* on the dining room veranda, while the purple shadows lengthened; moist-cooling gusts of wind heralding night from across the inlet; soft, buzzing mosquito-orchestras from under the lilac-bush back in the shadows. Memories from my childhood-land, recalled by the tingling dinner bell.

It was my grandfather's old school bell we were using— here as we had done in the archipelago during my childhood— calling all together for the evening meal, fittingly we thought. This grandfather of mine—my mother's father—had been a teacher in Bergslagen, too severe a teacher, according to some, yet greatly trusted with communal responsibilities; a zealous friend of the Lord's discipline, a guardian awesome in his anger.

That bell would undoubtedly have stories to tell. It would not have been acceptable to be stupid in that family—what would he have said could he have heard my son's halting, limited speech? What would he have said of Boel? Of my evasive replies, complicated explanations? He did not permit evasions

246

or excuses. You had to know your multiplication table. Preferably backwards also.

Now we heard his old bell, summoning us. A signal for the end of this long summer's joys. The obvious joys of childhood. With other children these joys would be supplanted with similar enjoyment in the family's autumn life and activity. Not so for Anders.

So we gathered noisily around the table—a few relatives who were our guests, the members of our family. Anders said the grace, it had become his duty. Perhaps a forgiving smile played on some face—it had not been our custom to pray together at the table—but all joined in, good-naturedly. There is something nice about saying grace, they might think. And tomorrow they wouldn't have to; little enough for today, the last day of summer.

But my personal depression found response around the table; I could notice it in the stealthy looks, in the muffled jokes. One young relative tried, haltingly:

"But Karin—wait 'til tomorrow! Cheer up tonight!"

And my cousin: "Better wait 'til tomorrow—it'll soon be dark. Better drive in daylight."

It would soon be dark. Why wait until it grew light? I needed the dark. And what did I have to wait for? What would change tomorrow? But explanations are so futile. Why try to explain the illogical, the apparently senseless? One knows one must act in a certain way. Better keep one's silence.

The packing had been a secret chore, almost on the sly. But now the bags stood there and could no longer be kept hidden. And the car must be backed out.

"Mummy sleep with Annis." He was climbing the stairs to the attic. The room with the old-fashioned rose-pattern wallpaper, and the gauze curtains. It had two beds. Tonight no one would sleep in them.

"Come on down, Anders. Mother and Anders go in the car."

He stopped still. He began to suspect.

"Annis don't want car."

"Only a little way."

"Annis not go car to Järna. Annis sleep here Noll-Wood."

247

"Another time, Anders. Come now and let's go."

The moon had already risen, August-round in a blue haze.

"Annis not go car. Annis sleep here. Dark outside."

All quite logical. Outside it was dark—that's when one sleeps. Obviously. Little children sleep when it's dark, they don't ride in cars. But if it should happen that their mother needs the dark around her. Then one must drive at night, even with little children in the car.

We drove through the last evening of summer, my son and I. Shrubbery and tall grass along the roadside appeared like dramatic stage settings in the car lights. It was a sort of theater. Something theatrical over this whole last evening, with trees and stones in sharp contours approaching us out of the blackness. Why so late, so late that small children ought to be in bed? Something had forced me to wait for the dark. It would be easier then. He might fall asleep in the car. At least he would have to go to bed as soon as we arrived. And the sleep would separate us. A long night would pass.

"Look at the moon, Anders. So sweet and nice."

"Moon go sleep. Annis not look moon."

"But the moon is very nice."

"Moon stupid. Mummy not drive car. Mummy stay home with Annis."

Quite logical. Mother ought not to drive in the dark, she ought to stay home with Anders. And as if the moon were agreeing it suddenly hid, as often happens out in the archipelago in August. The fog rises from the fields, drives in from the inlets and the sound, envelops the road.

I became frightened. Milk-white cotton-walls rose up on either side, the light beams cut through them in dangerously thin tunnels. Suddenly we met other lights, upon us almost before I espied them. How can it be? Such a sudden change. A few moments ago the moon, and now enveloped in this white unreality.

"Bad Mummy drive car. Mummy drive home. Danger Mummy drive."

"It isn't dangerous, Anders dear."

248

I slowed down, crept through the fog like a lost beetle, couldn't see the ditch. And the whole time I was amazed at his ability to draw conclusions. His logic. Everything was different with this one. They were not at all alike. And I had thought I knew all after my endless drives with Boel. I thought I knew: all children of this kind would love driving. How many times hadn't I said it? How many times hadn't we gone riding in the car—Boel, Liselott, and all the others? How many times hadn't Inger and I commented on how good it was for these children that they could go riding? The car was their greatest happiness in life.

Apparently that wasn't so.

And now the car was feeling its way along. Again something popped up in the fog-wall. I swerved, then I felt a jolt. We were no longer on the road; the wheels didn't obey—we were sliding off the road, and I turned off the ignition. The car was leaning precariously.

"Mummy drive home! Mummy stupid drive car! Very dangerous! Mummy and Annis drive to heaven? Car not go straight."

All this was new to me. Anders had never before spoken of driving up to heaven. He had never connected heaven with danger and car accidents. He understood what it meant when "the car not go straight." He was on the verge of crying. There was a pleading in his voice, stubborn accusation in its insistence.

I stepped out of the car to see how close we were to the ditch. The white-gray fog closed in around me, and I could see neither heaven nor earth. Only the small voice was coming through from the car, muffled as it were. Yet was I alone— the decision would be mine, not his.

"Annis and Mummy drive to heaven now . . . to heaven, Mummy! Annis and Mummy together. Not to Järna, Mummy! Drive to heaven!"

It was dangerously close, that stumbling abyss enticing. It would be sentimental if it weren't true, if it hadn't happened. But what actually happens is seldom sentimental. It can only be reported in various degrees of sentimentality. And I can report now that the temptation has never been greater than it was at that moment, the tiny voice persisting:

"Mummy and Annis drive to heaven now!"

It would have been so easy in the fog. So much easier to explain than "sleeping-pills," or any of the other means. The fog was actually as impenetrable as described in English novels. And the sea below, so close, so accessible. There was no sentimentality in this case.

This was the tempter.

Then I remembered a poem I had recently heard: "The greatest sin—to take the life that God you gave. . . . " I could hear it so clearly. I recognized all the arguments. I knew how all—or many of us with this fate—might have played with the thought, listened to it in secret moments, perhaps enjoyed it as one might enjoy the sweetness of forbidden fruit. But we always have to face this double consideration, three-double: our defective child, ourselves, and the others—our immediate dependents who perhaps need our aid, whom we must not fail. Perhaps they even love us. Anyway, it would hurt them. Have we then the right?

I shook myself in the fog and walked quickly to the edge of the road. Now I could hear the waves break below. How far below or how close I did not know. Nor how deep the water. It no longer attracted me. It had lost its interest.

Now I discerned also the only way to get the car off the shoulder and onto the road again. It would require great caution, but it was the one chance I had. Below me was the sea, the shoulder slippery from the August rains. I could so easily glide down. Especially the way the wheels were turned. And no one would suspect anything but an accident. But—I had made my decision.

At long last—with infinite caution to prevent the wheels from spinning—I put the car in gear and felt it gently work its way up the side. Then I knew that one must never give up.

"Annis drive heaven with Mummy."

"No, Anders, we are not driving to heaven this time. We're trying to get up on the road."

"Mummy not drive heaven, Mummy drive on real road."

250

When we approached the railroad overpass the remarkable happened suddenly—the fog lifted as fast as it had come. On the bridge the moon already shone through. And soon the stars seemed bigger and brighter than ever.

"Look at the stars, Anders!"

"The stars in heaven—not Mummy, not Annis, the stars and the moon in heaven."

Yes, the stars and the moon were in heaven where they belong. I pressed the gas pedal. Anders doubled up on a pillow in the back seat, now he wanted to sleep. He started to hum and roll, as is his custom. A custom he shares with so many of "our" children.

The motor was soon singing in rhythm with my thoughts, while Anders' humming gradually died down. I reached out and pulled the blanket over him.

There are so many roads, so many byroads—life can be lived in so many ways. Why should only I know the right road? It is my narrow circle that tells me my way is better than others. In India particularly I felt this so strongly, the limitation of our point of view. According to the social standards of our welfare state, the Indian masses live under wretched conditions, but with an acceptance unknown to us.

We put everyone in columns—catalogue, label, refer to this or that. Everyone must belong somewhere, have a number which indicates his value, where he belongs. Hadn't the Inconvenient One long ago given this answer better than anyone, illustrated it himself? I have never entirely been able to rid myself of the Inconvenient One and his accusations. A number is a sort of measure of our civilization. If one hasn't found a number, well, then one is inconvenient.

Yet only some hundreds of miles from us live millions and millions of people without our columns and labels. They have their own someone might suggest and refer to their caste-barriers. Indeed, every group creates its own systems. But the weak, the feeble ones, they are not left outside in the same way as here, I believe. They are part of the mass. Pearl Buck says in her book* concerning her "different" child, that the East takes it as a matter of fact, that idiots and imbeciles are an integral part of Far-East families. No one pretends they belong anywhere else. There is no criticism, no opinions expressed.

Perhaps it is no longer so out there—I know so little about it. I only suspect that it is our crushing effectiveness that creates our tight system, our narrow columns. Surely, those columns are bitterly narrow at times.

Now I was approaching the phosphorous-colored, greatly illuminated penal institution in the field beside the road. The fog was returning, played gently in the yellow searchlights back there, hovered over the depressing quadrangle. I shivered, even though the yellow lights threw a warm glimmer. A yellow light, penetrating the thickest fog, exposing every attempt to escape from one of these "bitterly narrow columns."

I found myself thinking of my father's mother who used to reside on the large estate not far from where I now was. My severe, imposing grandmother, who generously spread her husband's capably gathered fortune over the good and bad ones—she must have been a gold mine to any charitable organization.

With the yellow light coming to me now through the fog I could hear with my inner ear how she used to say: I feel sorry for thieves, my little girl. I feel sorry for them, for you must remember that God has made them the way they are—unable to distinguish between right and wrong. This you must always remember, and never judge.

Anders had awakened in the back seat; he raised himself and looked at the yellow lights. "Look!" he said. "Nice Christmas tree! Nice Christmas . . . "

"It is not a Christmas tree, Anders," I said, tiredly. "It is a place where they keep sick people. People who can't help they have been bad."

"Bad people. Bad people silly."

"No, Anders, you mustn't say that. They are sick. They

* *The Child Who Never Grew* (New York: The John Day Company), 1950.

252

can't help it that they must steal, perhaps even commit murder. It is a pity they have been created that way."

Anders lay down again.

"No Christmas tree, only bad men," he said. "Pity poor men."

The ability to feel sorry for someone, isn't this of utmost importance? For those other children it is especially important—perhaps the most deciding step they take toward our world—the moment they are able to feel sincere compassion. As we drove through the little community Anders had already gone back to sleep, but I was thinking of the "bad men" we should feel sorry for.

Perhaps they, all of them, lack this important something, compassion. The absence of it, above all, has placed them in the "bitter column" represented in our society by the phosphorous-painted quadrangle out in that field. The lack of feelings in the dangerous criminal—isn't that a greater handicap than any of the others? Emotional undevelopment—isn't this far more destructive than the weak ones' inability to excel intellectually?

Pity for the bad men.

I can see an important division line between what we call civilization and the wilderness of barbarism. The line is feeling, compassion.

When we arrived at Järna, Ingeborg had already gone to bed; some trouble with the telephone had prevented her from receiving the message we would arrive. But as is like her, she didn't complain about being disturbed.

I feel I have much to be grateful for after all. My children have a home here, a home that is warm, real—as a home should be. Of course, there are two of them, Boel and Anders; it is more than many can endure. But still there are so many things that bring joy; I opened the door to Boel's room and in the vague light I could see her face, almost sculpturally beautiful in its lines, the hauntingly attractive eyes now hidden under the heavy lids.

Boel does not suffer, she lives within the frame of her potentialities. She has been given a beautiful face, in some degree a compensation. She is inoffensive, good-natured in this world. Compassion is too complicated a function for her, but she is *good* in the land beyond, which is her world. She needs no qualifying functions there.

She is cut off, removed from what we call life, because our measures for life are different from hers. But she is given her fair face, her good nature, her soft dreamworld. These are her advantages, her great protection. There is so much she will never need.

Anders might have to face life in a much harder way; this I know and will ever worry about. Already he himself knows that he is different; he will grow angry over his shortcomings, his faulty speech, his inferiority with other children.

But is he capable of compassion? Has he a small place for more qualifying functions within the framework of emotions? I held his little hand in mine as we tramped up the steps to his room, where little Ragne already was asleep in his bed. My difficult moment was upon me, I held on to his hand, soon I would have to let go.

"Mummy stay Järna. Mummy sleep Annis' bed."

"Yes," I replied, emptily. "But now we must go to bed."

Mechanically I had let go of my usual deception. I was not strong enough to do anything else. And I knew deep within me that in the morning all would be right, without bitterness in his heart. He can always do it—the tears are on my side. All is well for him when morning comes, and he has forgotten that it might be different. The greatest hurt is in my heart.

And now my hard moment had come. We had said the evening prayer—Anders happy and pleased. But I?

I had not managed to keep back the tears. This day, summer's last day, my shell burst.

Then something happened.

Anders rose in his bed, ramrod-like, a tiny figure in blue pajamas that one day would be a man. He looked at me, he had seen my tears.

Now he took my face between his hands—now he had that finer feeling, compassion. His voice was soft:

"Mummy no cry! Poor little smallest Mummy! Annis comfort. Mummy go sleep, Mummy not cry. Poor little smallest Mummy!"

This happened unexpectedly—Anders took charge. He was the stronger, he wanted to comfort. He wiped away my tears with a new, tender self-importance, as if wanting to make up for not being like the others, momentarily forgetting his own shortcomings.

"Poor little Mummy, sleep now, in Annis' bed."

And perhaps having exhausted all his strength in his comforting effort, he abruptly lay down, pulled the blanket over his head, his teddy bear in his arms, and promptly went to sleep.

I stole out silently, needing none of the usual excuses this time. For a long while I remained standing, just staring at his door.

Not until I was back in the car, driving through the soft darkness homeward, did I fully realize what had happened up there at Anders' little bed. I re-lived it suddenly as a great gift, so intensely I had trouble steering the car because of the fog that now filled my eyes. Anders was still very little, but when I reached the yellow searchlights outside the penitentiary I felt convinced that he already had something those men in there were lacking.

He had shown compassion. He could feel sorry.

I felt very strongly then, this last summer evening, after having parted from my "Järna-family," that I must hold out. I must never give in, never fool with that thought again, that thought so tempting when the car had left the road.

I must never allow it again, for I had seen something important this evening. About Boel I know nothing except that she does not suffer. Not now. She is happy, I feel. Still happy.

And Anders. I must not fail. I had been given a new glimpse of our son whom I hadn't before clearly seen. He had taken a great, deciding step toward our world, perhaps it had been late in coming, but this evening he had shown it clearly. I felt it almost as a greeting from Grandmother who was able to retain compassion as a life principle, even after many tribulations—the greatest among them the loss of her three healthy children.

The car purred through the night, the radio playing late-hour sentimental pieces which were as soothing to my ear as Mozart or Chopin would have been at another time. I needed those sentimental tunes of my teen-age time. Escapist-music, perhaps, but comforting. A few lines from a poem by Erik Blomberg came to mind, written for just such an evening, I felt:

> Don't be afraid of darkness
> For light is resting there.
> How could we see the stars
> If darkness were not there?

This was my poem for the evening.

I felt rich, my son had displayed something important. He had taken a step toward our world. The words he had said: "Poor Mother!" the responsibility he had shouldered in comforting me, leads toward the world I will call ours. These words are not valueless in our world, they still count. We do not consider them empty, rather precious. And they made me rich. In spite of all, I am rich.

For Anders has shown compassion.